CELTIC MYTHS AND LEGENDS

CELTIC MYTHS
AND
LEGENDS

Michael Foss

Michael O'Mara Books Limited

First published in Great Britain in 1995 by
Michael O'Mara Books Limited,
9 Lion Yard, Tremadoc Road,
London SW4 7NQ

A CIP catalogue record for this book is available
from the British Library

ISBN 1-85479-695-X

1 3 5 7 9 10 8 6 4 2

Designed and typeset by
Keystroke, Jacaranda Lodge, Wolverhampton
Printed and bound in England by
Clays Ltd, St Ives plc

CONTENTS

1

WHO
ARE WE?

A blessing westward from me to Ireland,
Westward to the melodious waterfalls.
She is the mother who nursed us,
She is not uncomely to look on.
A blessing from me to Ireland,
An ancient land is this Land of Promise.

WHO
ARE WE?

The first name given to the land was Island of the Woods, and this name was given by a warrior of the people of Nin, son of Bel. Three times indeed was the island all one woodland, as the poet says: 'Three times Eire put coverings on her, and three times bareness off her.'

The second name was Land at the Limit of the World, and the third name was Noble Island. In the time of the Firbolg it had this name on it.

The fourth name was Eire, and this is from the name of a queen of the Tuatha De Danann who was in the land at the coming of the people of Mile into it. And the fifth and the sixth names were also from queens of the Tuatha De Danann, that is to say Fodhla and Banbha.

The next name was Inis Fail, the Island of Stone, which is the stone of destiny that the Tuatha De Danann brought with

3

them. It is a tabu-stone, for it used to roar under the person
fit to be king when the assembly of the men of the island met
at Tara. But it has not roared from the time of Conchobor
forward, for the false idols of the world were silenced when
Christ was born.

The next name was Isle of Mists, and the next was Scotia,
and then Hibernia, and after that Irlanda. This means the
Land of Ir, who was the son of Mile, and he was the first man
of that clan to be buried on the island.

It is said that the Greeks called the land Ogygia, which is
to say 'the most ancient land', and this is suitable, for it is a
long, long time since it was first inhabited.

> Green and flourishing is the grass of the island,
> Thick are her nut-sweet woods,
> Plentiful the fruit upon the smooth hills.
> To depart from her is a cause of misery,
> To leave her is ground for weakness.
> Sweet is the sound of her gentle wind –
> Green Banbha enclosed by woods –
> And sweet is the voice of her rivers.
> The speech of her birds is sleep-music enough,
> In that land abounding in salmon:
> Hail to the land of bright fountains!

It is the three daughters of the wicked Cain who inhabited
Ireland at first:

> Three virgin daughters of Cain,
> With Seth, son of Adam,
> They first saw Banbha.
> I remember their adventure.

Then three times fifty women came there, and three men.
Forty years they were in the island, till a plague fell on them
and they all died in a week. After that, Ireland was empty
desert for two hundred years until the Flood came.

But others say that it is Ceasair, daughter of Bioth, son of Noah, who came to Ireland before the Flood. Noah would not give a place on his ark to Bioth, Ceasair and Fintan. So they consulted one with the other.

'Will you follow my advice?' says Ceasair.

'We shall do that.'

'Well then,' says she, 'take to you an idol, and adore him, and forsake the god of Noah.'

So they got them an idol, and the idol told them to make a ship and put to sea – for the Flood surely would come, though none knew when. They made ready a ship and went to sea, and seven and a quarter were the years for them on the sea till they landed at Dunnamark, in the district of Corkaguiney, on the fifteenth day of the moon. And that was forty days before the Flood began.

Then about one hundred and forty years after the Flood, there came a youth of the family of Nin, son of Bel, to spy out the island. But the stay he made in it was not long. He went in the woods and returned to his people with plucked grass held in the full of his fist. But he made no stay in the island, which was not occupied till three hundred years after the Flood.

At the end of this time Partholon, son of Seara, son of Sru, of the family of Magog and of Japheth, came to occupy Ireland. And this was twenty-two years before Abraham was born, when the age of the world was one thousand, nine hundred and seventy-eight years.

On the fourteenth day of May, Partholon landed at Kenmare in the western part. And he had with him his wife and their three sons, and the wives of those sons, and a host of a thousand along with them. When they had gone through the island they settled on a little bit of land in the middle of the Erne, which was named Saimher after a lap-dog or whelp that Partholon killed out of jealousy of his wife. She did misconduct with her own attendant, Todhga, and made no apology for it but blamed the ill deed on Partholon and not on herself.

'O Partholon,' says she, 'is it possible for a woman to be

near honey, or a child next to new milk, or a cat smell fresh meat, or a workman see sharp tools, or a man and woman be close in private, without meddling the one with the other?'

In anger Partholon struck the little hound and killed it, as the old poet says:

> The king strikes the hound of the woman
> With his hand – is it not sad that it was so?
> The hound was dead.
> That was the first jealousy of Ireland.

But the cause that sent Partholon fleeing into Ireland was the slaying of his own father and mother, and for this reason God sent a plague on his race, even into Ireland. It did not go well for him and his people, for at last his followers were dead, nine thousand of them in one week at Ben Edar, afterwards called Howth.

After the destruction of the people of Partholon, Ireland was waste thirty years till Nemed, son of Agnoman, of the progeny of Magog, came to settle in the land. For every invasion of Ireland after the Flood was by some of the descendants of Magog. In the time of Sru, Partholon and the children of Nemed separated from each other, though well-related. And in the time of Seara, the Firbolg, the Tuatha De Danann and the children of Mile separated. But every tribe of these had the Gaelic tongue in their mouths, talking the one with the other.

Nemed journeyed from Scythia, between Europe and Asia. He gave his right hand to the mountains of Ural, till he came to the ocean of the north. Then he gave his left hand towards Europe, till he came to Ireland with thirty-four ships, and thirty persons in every ship of them.

Now, at this time sailors of the race of Cham, named the Fomorians, fared from Africa, fleeing to the islands of the west to make a settlement for themselves. Nemed won three battles over them and repulsed them. Then Nemed died of sickness, and the Fomorians revenged themselves with great oppression and slavery on his people. Conaing, for whom is named the Tower of Conaing, had many ships at

Tory Island in the north. He forced great tribute on the children of Nemed, to the extent that two-thirds of the children, and of the corn, and of the milch-cows of the men of Ireland were taken by the Fomorians every year in November, on the eve of the feast of Samhain.

Then the Fomorians put still more tyranny on the people of Nemed, that is to say they demanded of every household three full measures of the cream of the milk, of the flour of the wheat, and of butter, to be brought to Conaing's Tower on Tory Island. Liagh, the female steward of the Fomorians, enforced this tax throughout the land.

Rage seized on the men of Ireland, by reason of the heaviness of this tribute. Three good warriors among them, children of Nemed, raised an army and took Conaing's Tower, and they killed Conaing. But Morc, the Fomorian, brought ships from Africa to Tory Island and struck at the children of Nemed so that they resolved to fare away from Ireland, to escape the tyranny of the Fomorians. Most fled and left the rest in servitude to the Fomorians until the coming of the Firbolg, which was two hundred and seventeen years after Nemed arrived into Ireland.

After a long time, when the fleeing children of Nemed had withdrawn into Greece, the Greeks also put bondage upon them, forcing them to raise earth in sacks of leather, to place on the stony crags so that they might become fruitful soil. In this weary labour great sadness seized upon the people, and they resolved to make boats of their leather sacks and return into the west isles. So the people descended from Simeon Breac, son of Starn, of the family of Nemed, sailed back to Ireland after two hundred and seventeen years.

Towards noble Ireland set out the five sons of Dela – Slainge of the spears, Rudraige, Gann, Genann and Sengann. They made off at daybreak and Slainge, the elder, who was judge among his brothers, spoke as follows:

'Now is the time for effort, care and watchfulness.
Fierce and grey with foam is the sea.

7

Each fair ship sets forth from unendurable wrong.
The tyranny of the Greek is unaccustomed.
Let us strive to win the plains of salmon-bearing Ireland.'

Onward they sailed before a southwest wind, until they saw Ireland in the distance. Then the wind rose high and strong, and the waves drove against the walls of the ships, and the fleet was torn into three parts: the Firbolg, the Fir Domnann, and the Gaileon. The men of the Firbolg were named for the leather sacks they had used to carry the earth of Greece. The men of the Fir Domnann were named for the pits that were left when the earth was dug out. And the men of the Gaileon were named indeed for the darts or spears that were their weapons.

But all in one week they came into Ireland, and it is one conquest that they made, beginning on Saturday, the first day of August. When all the parties were landed, anxiously each sent out messengers, to gather all together at one place, at the stronghold of the kings at Tara. They all assembled and said to each other, 'We give thanks to the gods for our return to you, O Ireland. Let the country be divided equally between us.'

Thus it was that five portions were made, one for each of the sons of Dela, though all the people in all the parts were commonly called Firbolg, which is to say 'men of the leather sacks'. Thirty-six years was the length of the dominion of the Firbolg over Ireland. Their leader had the title of high-king, and none had that title before the Firbolg.

Now, there was another band of men descended from Iobath, third chief of the people of Nemed, who had departed from Ireland after the fall of Conaing's Tower. And these people were called the Tuatha De Danann. Some say they settled in Greek territory, around the city of Athens. There they learned their magic and their arts till they became skilled in every trick of sorcery.

On a certain time, the army of Syria made war on the

Athenians, and each day, however many Athenians were slain, it was those same slain soldiers who would rise up on the morrow and fight again. And this necromancy was done through the art and the magic of the Tuatha De Danann, who put demons into the Athenian bodies to restore them. So the Syrians took counsel with their own priests, who set a watch on the battlefield, and at the end of the fighting towards nightfall they thrust stakes of ash-wood through the bodies of all the dead enemies. On the morn, when the battle renewed, the dead bodies did not rise up but the demons fled out of them in the form of worms. Then the Syrians fell on the rest of the Athenians and slaughtered them.

As for the Tuatha De Danann, they departed in fear out of that land, and they did not stop until they came to the country of Lochlann, which is to say Norway. They got them four cities – Failias, Gorias, Findias and Murias – and placed four sages in those cities to teach the youth magic and arts. And their chief at this time was Nuada, son of Echtach.

After some time in those cities the Tuatha De Danann went to the north of Scotland, where they remained seven years. They had four noble treasures, which they brought from Norway. The first was the stone of destiny from Failias, the stone that used to roar under each king of Ireland at Tara. The second treasure was the sword that Lugh of the Long Hand used, and it was brought from Gorias. The third was the spear of that same Lugh, and from Findias it was brought. And the fourth was the cauldron of the great god Dagda, which none left unsatisfied, and from Murias it came.

Seven years the Tuatha De Danann spent in Scotland, then they came to Ireland. They landed in the country of Ulster on Monday in the first weeks of May, on the eve of the spring festival of Bealtaine. They burnt their boats, and the chance of retreat went away with the smoke and vapour of the burning ships. Then they put a magic mist about them for the space of three days, so the Firbolg who were in the land would not see them till they came to the Iron Mountain in Leitrim. Then they sent an embassy to the chiefs of the

Firbolg saying, 'Give up the kingdom of Ireland, or do battle for it.'

So they fought, one with another, at the two battles of Moytura, the first in Mayo and the second in Sligo. The Firbolg were overwhelmed and a hundred thousand of them slain.

As to the Tuatha De Danann, they are called 'the tribe of the gods who are the children of Danann', though some explain it otherwise. Certainly, they ruled over Ireland after the defeat of the Firbolg for one hundred and ninety-seven years, till the coming of the sons of Mile, who were of the family of Gaedhal and thus also of the progeny of Magog.

So all the invaders of Ireland were related one to another, and though they were enemies fighting for the land they all spoke the Gaelic tongue. And what was true to each was common to all, and so the great things of the people continued from the beginning to the end of time in Ireland.

THE PEOPLE OF
THE GODS ARRIVE

Eochaid, High-king of Ireland, saw a vision in a dream. He thought on it with wonder and perplexity.

'I saw a flock of black birds,' he told his wizard Cesard, 'coming out of the ocean. They swarmed all over us, and fought the people of Ireland. They confused us and destroyed us. But one of us struck the noblest of the birds and cut off a wing. Tell me, O skilful Cesard, what is the meaning of this vision?'

'Bad tidings for you,' answered the wizard. 'Warriors come from the sea, a thousand heroes covering the ocean. The speckled ships will swoop upon us. All kinds of death they announce, a people skilled in magic arts. Evil spirits will deceive you and hurt you, and they shall have victory over you.'

From their landing place in the north, at wide Tracht

Mugha in Ulster, the Tuatha De Danann marched through Ireland to the Red Hills of Rain, in the east of Connacht, and camped there. Their hearts were content at last, for they had reached the land of their forefathers.

When the Firbolg of Ireland heard of this arrival and went to find the invaders, they spied on the camp and saw the most handsome of mankind, well and fiercely armed, skilful in music and playing, the most gifted that ever came across the sea. Then the Firbolg were afraid, for the Tuatha De Danann – the tribe of gods of the family of Danann – excelled all the other peoples of the world in every art.

'It will be an advantage to have some report of those lads,' said the Firbolg. 'Who are they, and what are they up to? Where do they mean to settle? Let Sreng visit them, for he is bold to ask questions. He is big and fierce and uncouth and terrifying to behold.'

So Sreng rose up and went. He took his red-brown shield and two thick spears, his deadly sword and four-cornered helmet and iron club, and he went on his way to the Hill of Rain. And when the Tuatha De Danann saw such a huge fearsome man approaching, they sent large Bres, son of Elatha, to speak with him. The two men drew near, looking keenly but saying no word. Each was astonished by the grim size and the weapons of the other. So they crouched behind their shields and at last gave cautious greetings, for the same language, the sweet Gaelic, was in each man's mouth.

After they had talked, Sreng said: 'When you speak of your ancestor Nemed, your cheerful words gladden my flesh and my tongue. Your people and mine are brothers, both descendants from Simeon Breac. So bear this in mind. Humble your pride, let our hearts draw together. Remember our brotherhood, and save your own men from destruction. If we clash, many will be crushed most cruelly. 'Tis not an entertainment that will amuse.'

'Remove your shield and reveal yourself,' replied Bres, 'so I can tell the Tuatha De Danann about the look of you.'

'I'll do that,' said Sreng, and he raised his shield.

'Those weapons have a strange and venomous look,' said Bres.

'What do you see?' asked Sreng.

'Huge weapons, broad-pointed, heavy, keen-edged. Woe to him they should strike. Death is in their mighty blows, wounds in their hard plying, overwhelming is the horror of them. What do you call them?'

'Battle javelins are these,' replied Sreng.

'Good weapons,' said Bres. 'Bruised bodies they mean, gushing gore, broken bones and shattered shields, scars and ill-health. Death and eternal blemish they deal. Those who would use them have a fratricidal fury in their heart. It is better that we make a covenant.'

So they came together and talked.

'Where were you last night?' said Bres.

'At the holy heart of Ireland, in the hill-fort of the kings at Tara, with Eochaid, the High-king of Ireland, and the chiefs of the Firbolg. And where were you?'

'On the hill, in the crowded camp yonder on the mountainside, with the Tuatha De Danann and Nuada, our king, who come from the north of the world in a cloud of mist and a magic shower.' So Bres said, but he did not believe it.

'I'll go now,' said Sreng, 'it is a long journey that awaits me.'

'This is our message,' replied Bres. 'Tell the Firbolg to give battle, or to give up half of Ireland.'

'On my word,' said Sreng, 'I had rather give up half Ireland than feel the edge of your weapons.' So they parted in peace and fellowship.

When Sreng returned to Tara, the Firbolg asked him, 'What tidings?'

'Stout are their soldiers,' he replied, 'manly their men, bloody and battle-sure. Great and strong are their shields, keenly sharp their blades. Hard it will be to fight with them. 'Tis better to give them half Ireland, as they desire.'

'No,' cried the Firbolg, 'we shall not grant that, indeed. If we do so, they will take all the land in time.'

At about the same hour Bres reached his camp and told of his meeting with Sreng.

'A big, powerful, fierce, ugly lump of a man,' he said, 'with large and wonderful weapons. He is warlike and hard, without awe or fear of any.'

So the Tuatha De Danann set out to look for some strong place. They travelled westward over plains and rivers till they came to the back-end of the Black Hill, which is called Slieve Belgadain.

''Tis a good place,' they said, 'rough and strong and impregnable. From here we shall wage our war.'

And from this summit, as the poets sang, the Tuatha De Danann laid hold of Ireland.

Then Badb and Macha and Morrigan, battle-crows and sorceresses of the Tuatha De Danann, went to the Hill of the Hostages, and the Hill of the Gathering Host, at Tara. And they sent forth magic showers of sorcery and compact clouds of mist and a furious rain of fire, with a downpour of red blood on the heads of the warriors. They gave the Firbolg neither safety nor rest for three days and nights.

So the Firbolg gathered their armies in a place of meeting. From all over Ireland the warriors came, and they numbered eleven large companies. When they were ready they marched to the Plain of Nia where the Tuatha De Danann, with seven companies, had taken their position at the western end. Once again envoys met, for the discussion of their troubles. But they could not agree.

'Then,' said the envoys, 'must it be war?'

'Hold hard now,' cried the nobles of the Firbolg. 'Some delay is called for. We must prepare, for tattered is our mail, dented our helmets, and dull the edges of our swords.' So an armistice was arranged to make all ready for battle.

Now, while they waited, Ruad, with twenty-seven of the sons of brave Mil, sped westward to the end of the plain, to offer a hurling match to the Tuatha De Danann. An equal number came out to meet them, and then there was a mighty clash of arms and legs, till flesh was bruised and bones were broken, and some stretched out a silent length on the turf, and so the match ended. They raised a cairn on the field, and buried the bodies at Glen Carne Aillem.

When the preparations were done, Eochaid, the High-king, said to his poet Fathach, 'Go to the west and ask the Tuatha De Danann how the battle is to be fought. Is it for one day, or for many?'

'What we propose,' answered Nuada and the Dagda and Bres, 'is a long steady fight between equal numbers on both sides. Let us go on till you or we are under the earth.'

This was sad news for the Firbolg, as they had the greater army. So they sent for wise Fintan and took counsel. They put a trench around a great fort. Later, this was called the Fort of the Packs, from the packs of dogs that ate the bodies of the battle-dead, or the Fort of the Blood Pools, from the red gore in which the wounded lay. Nearby, they dug a Well of Healing, sprinkled with herbs, for the cure of the wounded. And the Tuatha De Danann also made a fort, called the Fort of the Onsets, and dug their own Well of Healing.

Six weeks of summer were gone when the day of battle came. The armies rose that day at dawn, and the early sun glimmered on bare blades. In close-packed companies, swept forward by stern-voiced commands, the armies advanced across the Plain of Nia. And it was Fathach, the poet of the Firbolg, who went between them, to sing of their fury and spread the report of it. He raised up in the middle of the plain a pillar of stone, and rested against it, looking east and west. Fathach's Pillar it is called now. From there, in anguish, the poet wept melancholy tears, and cried: 'What show, what glory, in the advance! On the Plain of Nia most terribly they clash. 'Tis the Tuatha De from the frozen north on that side, the Firbolg of the blood-etched blades on this side. Badb, drinker of the red gore, will thank them for bodies. Many will not return from their visit to Moytura. They will lie gashed, with heads cut off.'

Then the Dagda began the attack, hacking from the west through Firbolg ranks, cutting a wide path. When he saw this, Cirb raised his arm against the Tuatha De, hurling death, clearing his own large space. All day the battle went on, in combats and deadly duels. The seams of the shields were torn apart, swords wrenched from their hilts, rivets popped from the heads of the spears. A great many bold fellows stretched out on the turf for the never-ending sleep.

By the fall of the light the Tuatha De Danann were driven back and they retreated to their camp. The Firbolg did not pursue them but went cheerfully to their fort. Each warrior brought with him to the king a stone and a head, which they built into a great cairn. Then the magicians and the wizards on both sides brought crushed, healing herbs to scatter on the well-water. Thick and green was the healing water, and the wounded men rose whole out of it.

In the morning, strong armies well-refreshed came at each other again. Big blows were dealt, bosses of the shields were shattered, and spears twisted out of the hand. Swords broke on splintered bones, and agony-screams covered the battle-cries. When night fell the Firbolg were driven across the battlefield, though each still carried a head and a stone to Eochaid their king.

'Is it you who were beaten today?' said the king.

'It is,' said Cirb, 'but it will not profit them.'

Next day, as they set out, the Tuatha De Danann looked at each other, saying, 'Who shall lead us?'

'It is I who shall do it,' said the Dagda, 'for in me you have an excellent god.' And he went forth with his sons and brothers towards the ranks of the Firbolg, drawn up by their pillars and wooden props in the plain. And for this reason the field of battle was called Moytura, or the Plain of Props.

The Dagda started breaking men apart at this end, and Cirb the Firbolg was slaughtering brave warriors at that end, and each heard the battering blows of the other. Then they came together with furious slashes of their good swords, till at twilight Cirb fell. Then the Firbolg were thrashed to their fort, and the Tuatha De went homeward with a stone pillar and a head each, and they took the head of Cirb also.

In that same sad night came Fintan the wise, with his sons, to join the Firbolg. Thirteen bleak and hardy men, the sons

16

of Fintan came to Eochaid, the High-king, and they formed a guard of battle-scarred warriors, the world's trustiest troops.

A flaming mass was the fight on the next day, lurid in colour, gory of hand. Fierce it was and pitiless and terrible, hard-packed and close-knit, furious, ebbing and flowing with many adventures. The wizards and wise men stood on the pillars in high places, making magic, while the poets took account of great deeds and turned them into song. As for Nuada of the Tuatha De Danann, he was at the centre of things. And as for Sreng of the Firbolg, he was likewise in the middle. Death and blood pooled at their feet. All this Fathach saw from his pillar, as he stared east and west.

''Tis sure the Firbolg will lose many brothers,' he cried. 'Many will be the rolling heads and headless bodies on the plain. They fall by their shields. I'll trust no more to the strength of them while I stay in stormy Ireland. I am Fathach, the poet. Strongly has sorrow conquered me. Now that the Firbolg are falling, I surrender to the swift advance of disaster.'

Furies and monsters and hags of doom cried aloud, and their voices were heard in the rocks and waterfalls and in the hollows of the earth. It was like the agony of the last day, when all men will depart from this world. Some heroes still bestrode the battlefield, hacking with stout arms, like woodsmen. At the sight of them the armies stopped and wavered, falling away like water boiling over a kettle. A place was cleared around the great chiefs, and to them was left the battle.

Their feet churned the firm turf. Thirty bows were given and taken, till Sreng slashed at Nuada. His sword-thrust cleaved the rim of Nuada's shield and cut off the right arm at the shoulder. The king's arm lay in the dust, but the Dagda came quickly and stood over Nuada. Then the chiefs of the Tuatha De Danann caught up their king and carried him from the field, while the blood of the severed arm trickled on their bent backs.

The bad day was done and night's black shadow covered all. Then Nuada, the stricken king, spoke from a place of rest.

'Tell me, great Dagda,' he said wearily, 'how does the battle stand?'

'I will tell you, noble Nuada,' replied the Dagda, 'how stands the fight. Its calamities and disasters I will also tell. Our nobles fell before the violence of the Firbolg. Our losses are great, we can hardly count them. But Bres on our side, a warrior like a tower, made glorious carnage among the Firbolg, to the number of one hundred and fifty.

'Then huge Sreng was angered. He rained nine blows on your shield. It looked as if you could withstand him, O impetuous Nuada, but he hacked off your right arm! Then we were disheartened and many died, good men, warriors reeking blood-red wounds.

'Eochaid, High-king of the Firbolg, and his son Slainge the Fair, also did powerful deeds against us. But the High-king grew thirsty with blood-work and went wandering for a drink to the Strand of Eothail. There, three sons of Nemed surprised him on the silent sands. They fought, and all fell. Lugaid, your son, was killed, and Slainge the Fair, son of Eochaid, is likewise dead.

'After that 'twas Sreng that ruled the fight – many changed colour when they knew it – but still back and forth went the footsteps of the warriors, staggering, heart-hurt, though none turned and fled. Weary were we now on either side, so we stopped slaughter and went aside to pause and think.'

Sad, wounded and full of heavy reproaches were the Firbolg that night. Each one buried his kin and friends. They raised mounds over the brave men, and gravestones over the warriors, and tombs on soldiers, and hills over heroes. After that they took counsel, whether they should leave Ireland, or give battle again, or share the land with the Tuatha De Danann. They resolved to make one more fierce onslaught, though it hurt them sorely to think on it, as Sreng lamented:

> Resistance is destruction for men.
> We resolutely gave battle;
> There was clashing of hard swords,
> The strong plying of spears by noble warriors,

The breaking of buckler on shield.
Full of trouble are the plains of Ireland.
Disaster met us in the woods,
With the loss of many good men.

In the morning they made one more keen, murderous charge, a band of wild fiery men, their spears as close as bristles, cutting their way in a flame of fury against all opposition. When the Tuatha De Danann saw this, they drew back aghast and begged a time to talk.

'Let Sreng have the province of his choice,' they said. 'Let us stop this slaughter.'

All were agreed, and so they made peace. Sreng chose the province of Connacht, and the Firbolg took possession there. The Tuatha De Danann spread themselves in the other parts of Ireland and made Bres their king. Indeed he was High-king for seven years. But he died, after drinking unwisely in the heat of hunting at Slieve Gam. Then Nuada ruled again, for his stricken arm was magically replaced by the sorcery of his wise men, and he became the High-king.

THE
CONQUEST

The Tuatha De Danann were in the northern islands of the world, studying magic and sorcery, black skills, witchcraft and the arts of the druids, till in these things they surpassed all the wise men of the heathens. Then the Tuatha De made an alliance with the Fomorians. Balor, the grandson of Net, gave his daughter Ethne to Cian, the son of Diancecht. And she gave birth to Lugh, most glorious of sons.

The Tuatha De Danann came with a great fleet to Ireland to take it by force from the Firbolg. The Firbolg were defeated, their king Eochaid was killed, and a hundred thousand of his people also, as has been told.

But the hand of Nuada, king of the Tuatha De Danann, was cut off in the battle – it was Sreng, son of Sengann, that did it – so the physician Diancecht, with the help of Credne the

metal-worker, put on him a silver hand that moved as well
as any other.

Those of the Firbolg who had escaped from the battle fled
to the places of the Fomorians and settled in Arran and in
Islay and in Man and in Rathlin.

Now, there was a contention between the men and women
of the Tuatha De Danann regarding the kingship, for no
man who was not whole-made might be king. It was more
fitting that the king should be Bres, son of Elatha, though he
was not completely of the Tuatha De Danann. He would
draw them toward the Fomorians, the people of his father
Elatha.

The making of Bres came about in this way. One day, Eriu
of the Tuatha De Danann was looking from the house and
she saw that the sea was as flat as a plank. Then a vessel of
silver appeared to her, its size somewhat great but its shape
unclear, and the drift of the tide brought it to land. In it was
the fairest man, with golden hair to his shoulders, and a shirt
and a cloak trimmed with gold. A brooch of gold was on his
breast, five golden circlets about his neck, a sword with
inlays at his belt, and a brace of shining spears in the grip of
his hand.

'A fine time for love-making,' said the man.

'I've made no tryst with you,' she replied.

'What need for a tryst?' said he.

So they stretched themselves down together. When the
man rose, the woman wept.

'Why the tears?' he asked.

'Two things,' she said, 'I lament. One, that you possess me
now, though the youth of the Tuatha De have entreated
me in vain. Two, that you are leaving now.'

He drew a gold ring from his middle finger and put it into
her hand, saying, 'Part not with it either by sale or gift,
except to one whose finger it will fit.'

'Another sorrow I have,' said she. 'I know not who has
come to me.'

'No reason for ignorance there,' he replied. 'Elatha, king of the Fomorians, has lain with you. You will bear a son and let his name be Eochu Bres, that is to say Eochu the Beautiful. Every lovely thing to be seen in Ireland – field or fortress, ale or candle, woman or man or horse – will be judged by that boy, so people will say of it, "It is a Bres."'

In her time she gave birth to a boy and he was named as Elatha had said. In seven days he had made two weeks' growth, and in seven years he had the growth of fourteen summers. And when the contention arose among the Tuatha De Danann as to the kingship, Bres was made king. His mother Eriu gave him land, and the fort of Dun Brese was on that land, and it was the Dagda who built that fort.

But after Bres was king, three Fomorian kings put Ireland under tribute so that there was not smoke from a roof in Ireland that was not under this tribute. Even the champions of Ireland were pressed into service. Ogma carried firewood and the Dagda built ramparts and trenches, and he was the maker of Bres's fort.

Soon the Dagda was not happy with his work. He used to meet in the house an idle blind fellow called Cridenbel, whose mouth grew out of his chest. This Cridenbel thought his own ration was small and the Dagda's large. So he said, 'O Dagda, on your honour give me the three best bits of your meal!' And the Dagda, for the sake of honour, did so every night. But large indeed were the bits given to the satirist Cridenbel. Each piece was the size of a good pig, making in all a third of the Dagda's food. And the appearance of the Dagda was the worse for that.

One day the Dagda was working in the trench when he saw the Mac Oc coming to him.

'Very good, O Dagda,' said the Mac Oc.

'Even so,' said the Dagda.

'But you have a bad look about you.'

'I have good cause,' replied the Dagda. 'Cridenbel, that satirist, takes every night the three best bits of my meal.'

'It will not last,' said the Mac Oc. 'Soon you will finish your work, but seek no payment till the cattle of Ireland are brought to you. Then choose the dark, black-maned, lively heifer.'

When the work was finished and Bres offered a payment, the Dagda asked for the heifer, which seemed a foolish choice to the king. He thought the Dagda would have chosen something more.

All this time that Bres held the kingship, there was murmuring against him among the Tuatha De Danann, for their knives were not greased by him, and however often they visited him their breaths did not smell of ale. And there was no entertainment in the household from either poet or bard or satirist or harper or piper or hornblower or juggler or jester. They saw no races, no sporting contest, and only Ogma was there to prove his skill before the king. Yet his poor duty was only this: to bring firewood to the fort. Each day he carried a bundle from the islands of Clew Bay, but the sea snatched two-thirds of his load, because he was weak for lack of food.

On a certain day Corpre, poet of the Tuatha De Danann, came in his travels to the house of Bres. He entered a narrow, black, dark little house, with neither fire nor chair nor bed in it. Three small cakes he was given, and they were dry. On the morrow he arose, and he was not thankful. As he crossed the threshhold he made this chant:

> 'Without food quickly on a dish,
> Without cow's milk for a calf to grow on,
> Without a man's abode under the dark of night,
> Without pay for a company of storytellers –
> Let that be Bres's condition.

'There's no prosperity in Bres,' he added, and that was true. There was blight on him from that hour. And this is the first satire made in Ireland.

After this the Tuatha De met together to talk with their foster son Bres. It was agreed that he might remain king for seven years, so long as he gave proper sureties. As he was not willing to give up the kingship, Bres made this delay so that he might gather the *shee*, the magical warriors of the Fomorians, and seize the Tuatha De by force.

Then he went to his mother and asked where his family was. 'I am certain about that,' said she, and she gave him the ring that Elatha had left her. He put it on his middle finger and it fitted him.

Together they went forward to the lands of the Fomorians. The people there, as was the custom, put them to the test, making races and fighting in sword-play. When the dogs raced, the hounds of Bres were faster, and his horses too were faster than those of the men of the Fomorians. Then they came to sword-play. But as Bres lifted his arm to strike, Elatha recognized the ring on his finger and asked who he was, and Eriu told the whole story of his birth.

His father was sad for him and asked him, 'What need brings you from the land you ruled?'

'Nothing,' said Bres, 'but my own injustice and pride. I took their jewels and their land and their food. Until this time, none had taken from them tribute or payments.'

'That is bad for the telling,' said his father. 'Better their prosperity than your kingship. Better their prayers than curses. Why have you come here?'

'To ask for soldiers, since I mean to keep the land by force.'

'Gain it by justice only.'

'Well, then, here's a question: what advice do you give me?' asked Bres.

But Elatha would not help him and sent him instead to Balor, king of the Hebrides, and to Indech, one of the other kings of the Fomorians. And these kings gathered all the forces from Lochlann westward to Ireland, to impose tribute and rule by force, and they made a single bridge of ships from the Hebrides to Ireland. No host ever came to Ireland that was more terrifying than these warriors.

After Bres had departed towards the Fomorians, Nuada was once more in the kingship of the Tuatha De, for the physician Diancecht had put a silver hand on him that was as good as any other hand, and he was once more a whole man. So, in celebration, Nuada held a great feast at Tara for the Tuatha De

Danann. And there came before the doorkeepers of Tara a warrior and a company of strangers, led by a handsome, sturdy young fellow with a king's diadem on him.

'Who is there?' the doorkeepers asked the leader.

'Lugh Lonnansclech is here, son of Cian, son of Diancecht and of Ethne, daughter of Balor.'

'And you,' they asked the warrior, 'what is your art? No one without skill enters Tara.'

'Question me,' said the warrior, who was named Samildanach.

'Well?' replied the doorkeepers. 'Speak on.'

'I am a builder, I am a smith, I am a champion, I am a harper, I am a soldier, I am a poet, I am a sorcerer.'

'All those skills we have and need no more,' said the door-keepers. 'As for sorcerers, our druids and magicians and witches are as many as the sands of the beach.'

'I will speak further,' went on Samildanach. 'I am a physician, I am a cupbearer, I am a metal-worker. Ho, door-man, ask the king if he has anyone with as many arts and skills as I have. If he has, I will not enter Tara.'

One of the doorkeepers went to Nuada and said, 'The warrior Samildanach has come to court. He practises all the arts and is the master of every skill.'

Then the courtiers brought out the chess-boards of Tara, and Samildanach won every game. When all this was told to the king, he said, 'Let him enter, for never before has a man like him come into our fort.' And Samildanach went into the hall and sat in the seat of the wise man, because he was wise in every art. And in the evening he played on the harp, playing the music of sleep and lulling the king and the court into sleep from that hour till the same time next day.

When he saw this man's many powers, Nuada wondered if he might save them from the Fomorians. So the Tuatha De held a council, and the next day Nuada spoke with Ogma and the Dagda on Girley Hill, and the king summoned also his two kinsmen Diancecht and Goibniu. A full year they spent in close discussion, and then the druids of Ireland were called together, with their doctors and charioteers and smiths and landowners and lawgivers. They all spoke together secretly.

'What is your power?' the king asked Mathgen, the sorcerer. And Mathgen answered that he would shake the mountains of Ireland under the Fomorians till their summits fell to the ground. Then it would seem as if the twelve chief mountains of Ireland were fighting for the Tuatha De Danann.

'And three showers of fire,' added the druid Figol, 'I will rain on the faces of the Fomorians. I will take out of them two-thirds of their courage and skill and strength, and I will block up the bladders in their bodies and in the bodies of their horses. And the courage of the men of Ireland will increase with every breath. Even if they fight for seven years, they will not be weary.'

Then the Dagda said, 'That power that you boast, I'll wield it all by myself.'

'You are the Dagda, the Great God,' shouted the Tuatha De Danann. And the name Dagda stuck to him from then on.

So they prepared for battle. Lugh and the Dagda and Ogma went to the three gods of Danu, and they gave Lugh his weapons, which they had been making ready for seven years. At last, everything was in place and the Tuatha De heard the cry of Morrigan.

'Awake,' cried the taster of blood. 'Go forward to the remorseless fight!'

And the druids answered straight out, 'Yes, we will wage war!'

Now the Dagda had a house in Glen Edin to the north, where he had arranged to meet a woman. The river Unshin of Connacht roars to the south. He saw a woman by the Unshin in Corann, washing, with one foot in Aghanagh south of the water, and the other at Lisconny to the north. Nine loosened tresses hung about her head. The Dagda called to her and they lay together. Morrigan was the name of the woman, and the place where they lay was 'the Bed of the Couple'.

Morrigan told the Dagda that the Fomorians would land at Magh Scene, and that he should summon the Irish champions to meet her at the Ford of the Unshin. She would destroy Indech, king of the Fomorians, and take from him the blood of his heart and his manly testicles. Later, she gave two handfuls of that blood to the crowd waiting at the Ford of the Unshin. And its name evermore was the Ford of Destruction, because of the killing of the king.

When the Fomorians were landed, Lugh sent the Dagda to spy on them, and to try to delay them until the men of Ireland were ready. The Dagda went to their camp and asked for a truce. This was granted. But to mock him, the Fomorians made him a porridge, because his great love of porridge was well-known. They filled for him the king's cauldron, and poured into it four-score gallons of new milk, and the same amount of meat and fat. They put goats and sheep and pigs into it, and boiled everything together. Then they poured it all into a hole in the ground, and the king said the Dagda would be killed unless he ate it all. Never might it be said that the Fomorians were without hospitality!

So the Dagda took his ladle, big enough for a man and a woman to lie in it.

'If the taste of the broth equals the smell,' he said, ''tis good food.' Then he put the full-charged ladle to his mouth, saying further, 'It's a wise man that says "the poor bits don't spoil it".'

He ate and ate, and at the end of his hunger scraped a bent finger in the bottom of the hole amid the mould and the gravel. Then he fell asleep with a belly as big as a house, and all the Fomorians laughing at him.

When the Dagda awoke and saw the derision, he went away from them to the beach of Eaba. It was not easy for him to move owing to the size and tightness of his belly. The look of him was not pleasant to behold: a cape to the hollow of his elbows; a dun tunic around him as far as the swelling of his rump; a ragged hole in the tunic; two brogues on him of horse-hide, with the hair turned outside and his private parts in the air. Behind him he pulled a wheeled fork that was the work of eight men to move, leaving a track deep enough for the boundary ditch of a province, and this became known as the Track of Dagda's Club.

As he walked he saw a girl in front of him, fine-looking and of a good shape, with tresses of beautiful hair on her head. The Dagda lusted for her, but he was impotent because of his belly. The girl began to mock him, and to tussle with him. She hurled him so hard that he sank to his rump in the ground.

'Woman,' he said angrily, 'what business do you have, throwing me from my proper path?'

'My business,' she replied, 'is this: to make you carry me on your back to my father's house.'

'Who is your father?'

'It is Indech, a king of the Fomorians.'

Then she fell upon him again and knocked him here and there till the pit about his belly filled with the excrement of his body. And she mocked him with satires three times so that he would carry her.

Weary of this, he emptied the contents of his belly and climbed out of the hole, and the girl was waiting for him and mounted on his back. Then stones fell from his belt, or it may have been his testicles. Howsoever it was, she jumped on him and smacked him a smart blow across his rump, and as she did so her curly private hairs were revealed. So one thing followed another, and she gained a lover. They lay together and rubbed themselves together.

Then the girl said, 'You shall not go to the battle by any means.'

'Certainly I shall go,' said the Dagda.

'You will not, because I will be a stone at the mouth of every ford you cross.'

'That will be true,' he replied, 'but you will not keep me from it. I will tread heavily on every stone, and the trace of my heel will remain on every stone forever.'

'But still you will not go past me until I summon the Fomorians who are the sons of Tethra from the fairy-hills, because I will be a giant oak in every ford and in every pass that you must cross.'

'Indeed I will go past, and the mark of my axe will remain on every oak forever.'

Then the girl, the daughter of Indech, relented and said, 'Gather the men of Ireland all in one place and allow the Fomorians to enter the land. I shall hinder the Fomorians, and sing spells against them, and practise the deadly art of the wand against them. And I alone will take on a ninth part of their host.'

The Fomorians advanced to Scetne. The men of Ireland were in Magh Aurfolaig. The two armies were threatening battle.

'Those Irish have a determined look,' said Bres, 'I expect they mean to fight.'

'We'll give them the same medicine,' said the Fomorian king, 'so their bones will be crushed small if they do not pay tribute.'

The men of Ireland had agreed to keep Lugh from the battle. They feared his early death, which would extinguish the great number of his arts. Nine foster fathers were set to guard him. When the guards and the chiefs of the Tuatha De Danann were around him, Lugh said to his smith Goibniu, 'What is the extent of your power?'

'Not hard to say,' replied Goibniu. 'Though the fight be for seven years, every splintered spear, every broken sword shall be mended by me. My forged spearpoints will not miss their mark. The skins they pierce will not taste life afterwards. Dolb, the Fomorian smith, cannot do as much. I am prepared for this second battle at Moytura.'

'And you, physician Diancecht,' Lugh went on, 'what is your power?'

'Not hard to say,' said he. 'Any of our wounded, unless his head be off, or his brain struck open, I will make him perfectly whole by the next day.'

'And you, Ogma, champion warrior,' said Lugh, 'what is your power?'

'Not hard to say,' said he. 'Neither the king nor twenty-seven of his friends will be a match for me, I will win a third of the battle for the men of Ireland.'

'And you, Morrigan, battle-hag, what is your power?'

29

'Not hard to say,' said she. 'I stand fast. I shall pursue whatever I watch. I shall destroy those I have my eye on.'

'And you, sorcerers, what power?'

'Not hard to say,' said they. 'Those overthrown by our craft will show the white soles of their feet. We will take two-thirds of their strength, and prevent them from pissing.'

'And you, druids, what power?'

'Not hard to say,' said the druids. 'We will bring showers of fire on the faces of the Fomorians and sear their sight, so our warriors can kill them easily.'

'And you, Corpre the poet, what can you do in battle?'

'Not hard to say,' said Corpre. 'I will make a metrical malediction against them. I will name them and shame them, so by my spell they will offer no fight.'

'And you, Be Chuille and Dianann, my witches, what can you do?'

'Not hard to say,' said the witches. 'We will bewitch the trees and the stones and the sods of the earth so that they will appear like an army against them. And they will scatter in flight, terrified and trembling.'

'And you, the Dagda,' said Lugh. 'What power can you use against the army of the Fomorians?'

'Not hard to say,' said the Dagda. 'I will lay waste with heavy smiting and destruction and wizardry. Their bones under my club will be like hailstones under the hooves of horses.'

Thus the battle-ranks were drawn up, between fierce and proud men.

Then the Fomorians marched out of their camp in strong, indestructible battalions. There was not a soldier among them without armour against his skin, a helmet on his head, a broad spear in his hand, a sharp sword on his belt, a heavy shield on his shoulder. To attack them that day was like striking a head against a cliff, or putting a hand in a nest of snakes, or thrusting a face into the fire.

Balor and Bres led the Fomorians. On the other side, Lugh gave his guards the slip and took the forefront of the battle. In his chariot he led the Tuatha De Danann. He called to the men of Ireland to free themselves from the bondage of the Fomorians, for it was better to die for Ireland than to live and pay tribute. And to give them heart Lugh went around the warriors of Ireland on one foot and with one eye closed, and he chanted this spell: *Arotroi cath comartan. Fo, fo. Fe, fe. Cle. Amainsi!*

There was a great shout. The armies rushed together and started to hack at the one and the other. Many beautiful men fell in the stall of death. Great killing and grave-lying was seen there. Pride and shame were side by side, anger and indignation. Thick was the stream of blood over white skin. Harsh the tumult over the field: shouts and clashes and swishing and rattling and humming and whirring, and everywhere the clanging strokes of hard blows.

They attacked each other till their fingertips and toes almost met. Blood under their feet, and they slipping and falling down. A heavy, gory, hurt-inflicting, sharp, bloody battle, with shafts and blades red in the hands of foes.

Nuada Silver Hand fell before the blows of Balor. Then Lugh and eye-piercing Balor met in battle. An evil eye had Balor. That eye was never open save on the battlefield. Then four men would raise the eye-lid by a polished ring. Whoever looked in that eye, though they were thousands in number, were helpless. It had that poisonous power for this reason: once, when his father's druids were brewing magic, he looked in the window, and the fumes of the brew settled in his eye and gave it this dangerous power. Lugh and Balor came together, and Balor heard the challenge from Lugh.

'Now lads,' said Balor, 'lift up my eye-lid so that I can see this talkative fellow.'

The lid was raised from Balor's eye. Then Lugh hurled a stone from a sling-shot at him, which drove the eye through the back of his head, and it was Balor's own army that was looking at it. Balor fell on top of his own soldiers so that twenty-seven of them died under him, and the crown of his head struck the chest of his king so that a gush of blood spouted from his lips.

Then Morrigan came into the ranks with grim words, stiffening the hearts of the Tuatha De Danann to fight fiercely and resolutely. In a short time the armies broke apart, and the Fomorians were driven to the sea. Many called for mercy, and among them was Loch Half Green, the poet of the enemy. To him, Lugh replied, 'Grant me my requests.'

'That I will do,' said Loch. 'I will remove from Ireland forever all invasion and plundering by the Fomorians. And in all hard cases the judgement of your tongue shall resolve the matter until the end of life.'

So Loch the poet was spared, and he chanted to the Gaels 'The Decree of Fastening'.

After the battle, the Tuatha De Danann wished to kill Bres. But he stopped their hands, saying, 'It is better to spare me than to kill me.'

'What follows from that?' said Lugh.

'If I am spared,' replied Bres, 'the cows of Ireland will always be in milk.'

'Let us see what the wise men say,' said Lugh.

So Lugh went to wise Maeltne, who answered, 'He shall not be spared. Milk he might control, but what can he do about their age or their calving?'

'O Maeltne,' said Bres, 'a bitter alarm you give me.'

Then Lugh asked again, 'What else shall save you, Bres?'

'A harvest every quarter shall be yours, if you spare me.'

'No mercy for that,' replied Maeltne. 'It is not the proper way for us. What is suitable is this: spring for ploughing and sowing, summer for the growing of the grain, autumn for ripeness and reaping, winter for eating.'

'That does not save you,' said Lugh. And Bres cried out again, 'O Maeltne, another bitter alarm.'

But Lugh said, 'Less will rescue you.'

'What?' asked Bres.

'Answer me this: how shall the men of Ireland plough? How shall they sow? How shall they reap? Make known these things.'

'Say to them,' replied Bres, 'Tuesday for their ploughing, Tuesday their sowing, Tuesday their reaping.'

Thus Bres was spared and released.

Now, in the battle the champion Ogma found the sword of Tethra, one of the kings of the Fomorians. Ogma unsheathed the sword and cleaned it. Then the sword told him what it had done, because at that time it was the habit of swords to recount their deeds when laid bare. Therefore swords are entitled to the tribute of cleaning. By this means, many spells have been kept in swords from that time on, for demons used to speak from swords because men used to worship weapons, which were a safeguard of the people. And Loch Half Green, as was the custom, made a chant about that sword.

When the Fomorians fled, Lugh and the Dagda and Ogma went after them because they had carried off the Dagda's harper. After hard running they reached the hall where Bres and Elatha sat. There was the harp on the wall. It was the harp in which the Dagda had bound the melodies, so that it would not sound until he called forth the music.

Then the harp sprang from the wall, and it killed nine men altogether, and it came to the hand of the Dagda. Quickly he played for the Fomorians the three great musics: the sleep-music, the joy-music, and the music of sorrow. At the sorrowful music, the women wept. At the joyful music, the boys laughed. And at the music of dreams, the warriors slept. So the three were able to creep away unharmed, though the Fomorians had wished to kill them.

As they went away, the Dagda gathered up the cattle that the Fomorians had plundered. First he called to his dark, black-maned heifer, the one given him by Bres as his wages for fort-building. Then she mooed for her calf, and all the cattle of Ireland followed after her.

After the breaking of the battle and the cleansing of the slaughter, Morrigan, queen of war, proclaimed the triumph and the great victory to the royal hills of Ireland, to its spirit-army, to its water and rivers and estuaries. And the great deeds are still spoken of. 'What news?' the people call out. The reply comes, even from fierce Badb, the sister of Morrigan:

Peace up to heaven, heaven down to earth.
Earth beneath heaven, strength in each.
A cup very full, full of honey.
Mead in abundance, summer in winter.
Peace up to heaven.

That is the one side of the coin. But on the other side, she was also prophesying the end of the world, foretelling the evil of it, and every disease and every vengeance, and this is what she sang:

I shall not see a world that will be dear to me.
Summer without flowers, cows without milk,
Women without modesty, men not brave,
Conquests without a king.
Woods without mast, fishless seas,
Bad judgements by old men,
False precedents of the lawgivers.
Every man a betrayer, each son a robber.
The son will enter his father's bed,
The father also in the bed of the son,
A brother becomes his own brother-in-law!
None will look for a woman outside his own house.
O evil time, deception, deception.

2

THIS WORLD, THE OTHERWORLD, AND THE FATE OF MANKIND

O you that plant the tree,
Who shall live to pluck its apples?
When the bright shoot is grown,
Are you the one to see it?
Death has made even this doubtful.

THE FATE OF THE
CHILDREN OF TURENN

In the time when Nuada of the Silver Hand ruled over the
Tuatha De Danann, the Fomorians from Lochlann in
the north oppressed the people of Ireland and took a
heavy tribute: namely, a tax on their bread-troughs, and on
their millstones, and on their baking-pans, and on top of this
was an ounce of gold from each man besides. This tribute
was paid each year, on the Hill of Usnech, and those who
would not or could not pay had their noses cut off them.

Before the paying of the tribute, a great assembly met on
the Hill of Usnech, to the west side of Tara, and it was not
long before they saw an armed band from the east, with a
young man in command, and the brightness of his face was
like the setting sun, which was hard to look on. Then they
knew him for Lugh Lamfada – Lugh of the Long Hand – and

with him were the warriors of the *shee* from the Land of Promise, and his own foster-brothers, the sons of Manannan Mac Lir, the god of the sea.

And this is the way Lugh was: under him was Manannan's horse, Enbarr of the Flowing Mane, that was as swift as the naked cold wind of spring, and the sea and land were all one to her, and no rider was ever killed off her back. He had on him Manannan's breastplate, that kept the wearer from wounds, and the jewels of his helmet flashed like the sun on a summer day. At his side was Manannan's sword, the Answerer, that let none escape it in battle, and against it a man had no more strength than a new-born babe.

Nuada and the Tuatha De Danann welcomed these warriors, and it was not long before they saw another troop advancing. It was nine times nine surly, slovenly messengers from the Fomorians come to take the tribute from the men of Ireland.

'Why do you salute that surly band,' Lugh asked Nuada, 'when you did not rise up for us?'

'It is needful to do so,' replied the king, 'for even a child sitting before them would be a cause for killing.'

'Truly,' said Lugh, 'there is a strong desire upon me to kill these fellows myself.'

'That is a thing would harm us greatly,' said Nuada, 'for we would bring our own death and destruction on us.'

But Lugh shouted, 'Too long has this oppression lasted!'

With that, he attacked the Fomorians, dealing red slaughter to eight nines of them. But he let the last nine go, saying, 'I would kill you also, but it is safer that you take a message to tell your own country what you have seen.'

So that nine went back to Lochlann and told their story, which made the Fomorians wonder.

'Who is this young man?' said Balor of the Evil Eye.

'I know him well,' said Ceithlenn, his wife. 'He is Lugh of the Long Hand, son of your daughter and mine. It was foretold that he would bring to an end our power in Ireland.'

Then the chief men of the Fomorians took counsel, with their nine poets, and Lobais the Druid, and Balor himself, and his twelve white-mouthed sons, and Ceithlenn of the Crooked Teeth. At this time also came Bres, son of Elatha, to ask help from the Fomorians.

'Give me seven battalions,' he said, 'and I myself will go to Ireland and fight this Ildanach, this Master of All Arts, this Lugh. I will strike off his head and bring it to you here.'

Without delay all was made ready to set out for Ireland, with men and grim weapons sent on their road by Balor's high words.

'Give battle to Lugh,' he cried, 'and strike off his head. Tie that land called Ireland to the back of your ships, and let the indifferent waters rest in its place. Put it on the north side of bitter-cold Lochlann, far removed from the Tuatha De Danann till the end of life and time.'

Then the Fomorians set their painted sails towards the untilled acres of the wide-lying sea and held course for Eas Dara. Then the Fomorians went westward into Connacht, destroying it through and through. The king of Connacht at that time was Bodb Derg, son of the Dagda.

But Nuada of the Silver Hand was not minded to avenge the wrong done to Bodb Derg, and Lugh became angry with him. So Lugh himself rode westward out of Tara. He had not gone far when he saw his own father Cian coming with his uncles Cu and Ceithen. These three were the sons of Cainte.

'This is early rising, Lugh,' they called. And he replied, 'Good cause for it. The Fomorians are here and have robbed Bodb Derg. Go gather the warriors of the *shee* from every hidden place where they live.'

Away they went, south and north. Cian had reached the plain of Murthemne when he saw the three sons of Turenn, the son of Ogma. Between the sons of Turenn and the sons of Cainte there was hatred and bitterness, and if they were to meet, fighting would surely break out.

'If only my brothers were with me, it is a brave fight we would make,' said Cian to himself. 'But now it is best for me to draw back.'

He saw a herd of pigs nearby, so he touched himself with

a druid's wand. He changed himself into the shape of a pig and rooted in the ground with the rest.

But Brian, the eldest of the sons of Turenn, saw what had happened. Fearing that this might be the magic of an enemy, he touched his two brothers with his own druid's wand, turning them into thin, fast hounds that yelped in the track of the enchanted pig. They chased that pig into the edge of a wood where Brian threw a spear right through the pig's body.

'Evil is this thing you have done to me,' cried the pig, 'since you knew it was me.'

'It seems to me,' said Brian, 'you have the talk of a man.'

'Certainly,' replied the pig. 'I am Cian, son of Cainte. So give me your protection.'

'I swear by the gods of the air,' said Brian, 'if you had seven lives I would take every one.'

'Is that the way of it? But grant me this: let me go into my own shape again.'

'That we grant. It is easier to kill a man than a pig.'

Then Cian took his own shape and said, 'Though you give me no mercy, I shall have the best of you. The blood-money for a hog is nothing much. But kill me as a man and you shall pay the heaviest penalty ever put on a person. The very arms you kill me with shall tell the tale to my son Lugh.'

'No weapons shall kill you,' said Brian, 'but the stones on the ground shall do it.' With that, Brian and his brothers smote him so fiercely with great rough rocks that they made him a poor bloody pulp and buried him a man's height down in the field. But the earth would not take him and cast him up. Six times the sons of Turenn buried Cian, and six times the earth spat him out. But on the seventh time the earth closed over him and received him. Then a voice sang from below the ground:

> The blood you have spilled,
> The hero you have killed,
> Shall follow your steps
> Till your doom be fulfilled.

40

Now, when Lugh of the Long Hand had brought help to Bodb Derg in Connacht, and they had won the battle against the Fomorians, Lugh looked for his father Cian. 'If he were alive,' thought Lugh, 'surely he would have been at the battle. Neither food nor drink will I take till I know his fate.'

With the warriors of the *shee*, Lugh went about the country till they came to a place where the earth spoke and said, 'Lugh, here your father was in great danger, as he saw the sons of Turenn before him. Into the shape of a pig he went, but they killed him in his own shape.'

So Lugh and his men dug in that spot, to know what manner of death had been put on Cian. They raised the body tenderly from the grave, and it looked all one bed of wounds.

'O sons of Turenn,' Lugh groaned, 'you gave my dear father an enemy's death.' He kissed his father three times, and then he began to lament.

'I myself am a poor thing after this death,' he cried, 'for my eyes do not see, and my ears do not hear, and the pulse of my heart is stopped. O gods, why was I not here when this thing was done? The Tuatha De Danann have done treachery one on another. Loss and weakness will hound them now. East and west, all Ireland will not be free from trouble.'

Then they put Cian under the earth again, and spilt tears above the grave, and a stone was raised with his name on it in Ogham.

'The sons of Turenn did this thing,' said Lugh, 'and grief and anguish will fall on them from it, and on their children. It is no lying story I tell you. Have pity for the way I am, for the heart is broken in me since Cian, the dear man, is no longer living.'

Then Lugh returned to Tara and sat in the king's high seat. Before him he saw the three sons of Turenn. They were beyond all others for beauty and skill, for a bold hand in battle, and an honourable name. Lugh looked down and shook the chain of silence, and all listened.

'I have a question to ask,' he said. 'What vengeance would you take on a man who killed your father?'

There was great wonder in the crowd. They looked from one to another till a certain chief said, 'Is it your own father you speak of?'

'Indeed it is,' said Lugh, 'and I see here the men who killed him. No simple death in a day would I give his murderer, if I had him, but I would cut off his limbs day by day till I made an end of him.'

'We would do the same,' cried the chief men, and the sons of Turenn were among them.

'If I myself had killed your father,' said Nuada the king, 'I would be well content to pay the blood-fine.'

At this, the sons of Turenn muttered together, 'Let us tell of the killing.'

So said Iuchar and Iucharba. But Brian, the eldest, answered, 'I am in dread that he will not agree to a fine, if we acknowledge the deed.'

'Nay,' said his brothers, 'speak out. Tell of the killing.'

Then Brian spoke out, and Lugh agreed to impose a fine.

'This is it,' said Lugh, 'though it may be too much for your burden: three apples, and the skin of a pig, and a spear, and two horses with a chariot, and seven pigs, and a whelp-hound, and a cooking-spit, and three shouts on a hill. All that is the fine I am asking.'

'It is not too much,' said Brian, 'not by a hundred times. And we are thinking, because of its smallness, that you have some treachery behind it.'

'Not so,' said Lugh, 'I will ask no other thing. So let us pledge.'

Then the sons of Turenn bound themselves by the king, and by the son of the Dagda, and by all the chiefs of the Tuatha De Danann, to pay that blood-fine to Lugh.

'Now, for your better understanding of the fine,' said Lugh, 'this is the way it is: the three apples are from the Garden in the East of the World, the most beautiful and most virtuous of all apples. They are the colour of burnt gold, and the size of the head of a child, and the taste of them is like honey, and they take away the pain of wounds and sickness. Then the skin I ask is the pig-skin of Tuis, King of Greece, that overcomes all danger and turns running water into wine. I am thinking that it will not be easy to get it without leave.

'As for the spear you will seek, it is the very deadly spear of Pezar, King of Persia. The Slaughterer it is called. Its fiery head is kept in a cauldron of water, to save the palace from burning. And the other things I ask, would you know about them? The two horses and the chariot belong to King Dobar of Sicily. And the seven pigs, which will never know death, are those of King Easal of the Golden Pillars. And the whelp called Fail-Inis belongs to the King of the Cold Country, and this little hound is as beautiful as the sun so all wild beasts fall down at the sight of her. And the cooking-spit is that of the wild women of Fincara, where each woman is a match for three good warriors. And the three shouts you must give will be on the Hill of Midkena, in the north of Lochlann, where the people are under the holy injunction of a *geasa* never to shout. My father Cian got his learning with these folk, and even if I would forgive you his death, they would not. That altogether is the fine I set upon you.'

These were magical things, and among them were the things that Lugh needed for the final defeat of the Fomorians.

When they heard all this, there was silence and darkness on the sons of Turenn. In their doubt, they went to ask their father what to do. He told them that they needed the help of Lugh himself, or failing that at least the loan of Manannan's powerful possessions.

'You shall not have Enbarr, the horse of the flowing mane,' Lugh replied to their asking, 'but I'll grant you the loan of Manannan's boat, the *Wave-Sweeper*.'

Then the sons of Turenn went sadly away, with their sister Ethne, to Brugh of the Boyne where the boat was.

'O dear brother,' said Ethne to Brian, 'it was an evil thing you did, to kill the father of Lugh. Whatever harm may come to you, it is but just.'

'Sister, do not say that. We are in good heart and will

do great deeds. Better to be killed a hundred times over than to meet the death of a coward.'

'Grief and sorrow overwhelm me,' said she, 'to see you driven from your own fair land.'

The three sons of Turenn launched their boat from the sweet shores of Ireland. The *Wave-Sweeper* did not neglect their orders but sailed forward over the green-shaded waters and the deep places.

'Let us make straight to the things we need and attack them,' said Iuchar and Iucharba, 'and bring them away or fall ourselves, since we cannot escape the dangers before us.'

'Better that our story of bravery and skill be told after us than for folly and cowardice to hang on our names,' Brian agreed. 'Let us go in the shape of swift hawks into the Garden of the East, and snatch the apples in our claws, and make a quick flight away.'

With the touch of their druid's wand they became hawks. Boldly they swooped on the apples and bore them out, though the daughters of the Garden turned into sea-eagles and scorched the hawks with lightning before the sons of Turenn reached the safety of their boat.

Then they swept over the pathless seas to Greece. 'We shall arrive here,' said Brian, 'as poets of Ireland. In that way the lords of Greece will hold us in honour.'

'It will not be easy for us,' said his brothers, 'without a poem, and little enough we know how to make one.' But they resolved to try. They tied their hair in the fashion of poets, and went to the door of the court.

So in went the sons of Turenn, having the look of poets, and they fell to drinking and pleasure without delay. They had never had such a grand time, nor seen a better household. But after a while the king asked them for a poem.

'We have no poem,' they said to each other. 'The only poetry we know is to take what we want by the strength of our hands.'

'We must do better than that,' said Brian. So he rose up and spoke in this way:

> 'O Tuis of Greece, we do not hide your fame.
> We praise you as an oak among kings.
> The bounty I ask as a reward,
> It is but the skin of a pig.'

''Tis a good poem,' said the king, 'a grand poem. But I know not a word of the meaning.'

Then Brian explained the hardness of the poem, which was to say that he would have the pig-skin of the king or there would be trouble between them.

'Indeed the hard meaning is now clear,' said the king, 'but you talk too much of my pig-skin, O poet of Ireland. I would not give it up for all the poets of the world. But as the price of your poem I will give you as much gold as will cover the pig-skin three times.'

The skin was brought into the court. But as the gold was being measured out, Brian snatched the skin with his left hand and struck the keeper with a slash of his sword, making two halves of him. Then Brian threw the skin about him and the three brothers ran from the court, cutting down all who opposed them. They sprang to their boat and left the blue streams of Greece behind and sailed to the border of Persia.

The trick of the poetry had been a good trick in Greece, so they tried it again with King Pezar in Persia. But when the king learnt the inwardness of the poem, that Brian wanted the fiery spear, Pezar was angry.

'You have little sense to ask me that,' he said. 'Only respect for poetry stops my soldiers from killing you on the spot.'

When he heard this, Brian threw one of the apples from the Garden of the East, as round and heavy as a large stone, straight at the king and dashed his brains out at the back of his head. In the wink of an eye, the sons of Turenn had the spear in their hands and their heels were flying on the path to their boat.

Now the luck of the adventure was running with the sons of Turenn. They had little trouble taking the chariot and the two horses of the King of Sicily, and they drove away like the cold spring wind over both land and sea. King Easal, for fear of the three brothers, quickly gave up the seven pigs and sent them on their way in the company of friendly ships. But the whelp-hound, Fail-Inis, was not won without swords, and they left that Cold Country with blood on their hands.

At this time it was told to Lugh of the Long Hand that the sons of Turenn had already won all the things needful for the final battle against the Fomorians. So he sent a druid's spell after them, to make them forget for the time being the rest of the blood-fine. The spell settled on them and they had a great longing to see Ireland again, so they turned home with their whole task undone.

Lugh awaited them at Tara, and the smooth armour of Manannan was on him, and the enchanted cloak of the daughters of Flidas was over his shoulder. Then Lugh stepped out on the green grass and Nuada gave him the things of the fine collected by the sons of Turenn.

Lugh took the things he wanted. Then he said further, 'All this is good payment for a death. But there is something wanting yet. Where is the cooking-spit? And when did you give the three shouts on the hill?'

The sons of Turenn were sad when they heard this. Clouds of weakness covered them, and they were again in grief and darkness. On the morrow, their sister Ethne took them once more to the sea-banks, and again she was lamenting.

'Brian of my life,' she cried, 'where is the pity for you, where is the pity for the sons of Turenn? O salmon of the Boyne, O salmon of the Liffey, since I cannot keep my brother here I am loath to part from him. O Rider of the Wave, your enemy intends that you should not return. But your going is cause for pity. This heavy morn my eyes are filled with tears.'

Once more the sons of Turenn cast off onto the waves of the unforgiving sea. In a quarter year they had gone far from men, and then Brian put on his water-clothes and walked in the sea, looking for Fincara, the Island of Fair-Haired Women. He found it and went to the court, but all he saw was a band of women sewing and embroidering. In their midst was a bright cooking-spit lying on the table.

As he snatched up the spit the women began laughing and called out to him, 'That's a brave deed for your hand. The least of our women could make you hop most painfully, you and your brothers also. But for all that, we like the look of your daring, so take the spit along with you, and good luck to you.'

Brian bade them farewell and returned to his brothers just as their hearts were beginning to fail at his absence. Then away they sailed to the north of the world to look for the Hill of Midkena. After they landed, and the guardian of the hill saw them coming, he set on Brian, and the two of them fought like champions till the guardian fell dead. Then the three sons of Midkena fought the three sons of Turenn, and you might come from the Eastern End of the World without seeing a better fight for greatness of blows and courageous spirit. The men of Midkena drove their spears into the sons of Turenn, but that hardly stopped them at all, and they lodged their own spears fast in the bodies of the enemy so that the men of Midkena fell into the swoon and faintness of death.

But the sons of Turenn were sorely hurt. 'Dear brothers,' said Brian, 'how is it now with you?'

'Certainly, we are near death,' said they.

'Rise up then,' replied Brian, 'and give three shouts on the hill, for I feel the mist of death descending.'

Brian raised up his brothers, all of them leaking blood like storm-driven ships on the rocks, till three painful shouts rang on the hill. When that was done, they crawled to their boat, and they were travelling the sea for a long time with faintness and heartache upon them.

At last, Brian called out, 'I see Ben Edar, and the Hill of Howth, and our father's fort, and Tara of the kings.'

'Ah, we should have our fill of health,' said his brothers, 'if only we saw that. Raise up our heads, dear brother, till we see Ireland again. Then life or death will be the same to us.'

In the evening they came to Ben Edar and were carried to their father's house. Brian gave the cooking-spit to his father and told him to take it to Lugh. And he begged his father to bring back the pig-skin of Greece that had the healing of bodies in it.

'Ask for it,' said Brian, 'for the sake of friendship, for we are of one blood. Let him not return hardness for hardness. And dear father, be quick on the journey, or you will find us gone before you.'

But Lugh of the Long Hand denied them the pig-skin. He would not give it up even when the father returned to Tara carrying on his back the pitiful figure of Brian.

'You shall not have the skin that heals,' said Lugh. 'If you offered me as much gold as would span the world, I would not take it from you. It pleases me that death shall come to the sons of Turenn, in payment for the deadly deed they have done.'

When Brian heard this, there was no remedy but to go to the place where his two brothers lay. He rested between them, and the life went out of all three of them at the same time.

THE FATE OF
THE CHILDREN OF LIR

After the battle of Tailltin, when the Tuatha De Danann chose a king for the five provinces of Ireland, Lir heard that it was given to Bodb Derg, son of the Dagda. Lir went away with his mouth closed, for he thought he had a right to be king. The others were wishing to attack him, and burn his house, but Bodb Derg stopped them.

'That man,' he said, 'knows how to defend himself. Besides, I am still king, despite him.'

And so it rested. After a while Lir's wife died from him. That came very hard on Lir, and there was heaviness on his mind. There was great talk of the death in all Ireland, and the news came to the house of Bodb.

'If Lir minded it now,' said he, 'I could do him good friendship. I have here with me the three girls of the best shape, and the best appearance, and the best name in all Ireland:

that is to say my own dear foster-children Eve, Eva and Alva, the daughters of Ailill of Aran.'

The Tuatha De Danann said these were good words, and a message was sent to the house of Lir to say, 'If you have a mind to put yourself under the rule of the son of the Dagda, he will give you one of his foster-children for a wife.'

The offer pleased Lir. He set out next day with fifty chariots from Shee Finnaha, and he went every short way till he came quickly to Bodb's house on Loch Derg. There was a fine welcome for him and merry attendance that night.

The three daughters of Ailill were sitting in the hall, as quiet as you please, and Bodb said to Lir, 'Take your choice among them there, my three pretty nurslings.'

Lir saw them all and then looked aside. 'I cannot say which is my choice,' he replied. 'But she who is the oldest is the noblest and the best for me.'

That night, he chose Eve, the eldest, for his wife, and at the end of two weeks took her away to his own house for the wedding-feast.

In good time Eve gave birth to two children, a daughter and a son, whose names were Finnola and Aed. Then she was brought to bed again with two sons, Fichra and Conn. But she herself died in this childbirth, to the grief of Lir. Only that his mind was tender for his four children he would have gone near to death for sadness.

There was wailing among the people for her death, and Bodb Derg also lamented.

'We grieve this death,' he said, 'for our daughter's sake, and for the sake of the good man whom she bound to us. But I will stay ever close to him and give him now for wife my foster-child Eva.'

Lir came for the girl, and married her. And Eva held her sister's children in honour and affection. Certainly, no one at all could see those four mites without giving them the heart's love.

Bodb Derg came often to Lir's house for the sake of those children, and he took them often to his own estate. About this time the Tuatha De Danann came to celebrate the Feast of Age on the Hill of Shee Finnaha, where Lir was, and the beauty of those four children was a joy to everyone. Lir was glad in the sight of his children, and rose up at daybreak with them, and lay down among them at night.

Soon a fire of jealousy was lit in Eva, and she formed a hatred for her sister's children. She let on to have a strange sickness that lasted nigh a year, and all the time she was planning a cruel treachery against the children of Lir. She put the children in her chariot, as if to go to the house of Bodb Derg. On the journey, she took aside the guards and soldiers.

'Kill now the children of Lir, who have displaced my love in their father's breast,' she said. 'Then choose your reward from the good things of the world.'

'This is a bad deed you thought of,' they replied, 'and harm will come to you from it.'

So she took a sword herself, to kill the children. But being a woman with no good courage and no strength in mind she could not do it.

They continued their journey westward to the Lake of the Oaks, in Westmeath, and stopped there to rest. It was a hot day, so Eva told the children to swim in the lake, and they did so willingly. As soon as Eva saw them in the clear water she touched them with a druid's wand and put them into the shape of four white swans.

'Off with you,' she cried, 'on the water's wave, your luck is gone forever. Let your friends be sorrowful, but your laments will be lost in the clamour of the birds.'

'Witch,' Finnola called out, 'it is a bad thing you have done, and an evil friendship, to destroy us without cause. But vengeance for it will come upon you from those who love us. Tell us at least the bounds of this enchantment. When will it stop?'

'It will be the worse for you that you asked me,' said Eva. 'But I will tell you: three hundred years here on smooth Lake Darvra, and three hundred years on the Sea of Moyle between Ireland and Scotland, and three hundred years in the west, between Erris and the Isle of Glora – all these are to be your journeys. And your time of enchantment shall not end till the prince of the North weds the woman of the South.'

Then Eva repented a little, before these faces so sorrowful.

'There is no other help,' she said, 'to give you now, except you may keep your own Irish tongue. You will still be singing the sweet music of the magic *shee*, to lull men to sleep, and there will be no music in the world equal to it. You will keep also your sense and your reason, to lighten the load of your animal shape.

'Now go your way from my sight, you children of Lir, with your faces so pale and your Irish murmuring. Nine hundred years will you be on the waters, and a long time of pain it is indeed. The heart of Lir, that man of many victories, is now no more than a husk of death. His groaning will be a sickness to me, though it is I who have done this treacherous act.'

Then she whipped up the horses of the chariot and rode on to the house of Bodb Derg where there was a welcome for her.

'But where are the children of Lir?' said the son of the Dagda.

'I will tell you that,' said she. 'Lir has no liking for you. He will not trust them with you, for fear you might keep them altogether.'

'That is a wonder indeed, for those children are dearer to me than my own.'

He thought it was the deceit of the woman that had caused this, so he sent messengers to Shee Finnaha.

'Your children are not come to the house of Bodb Derg,' they said to Lir, 'and Eva says it is yourself who withholds them.'

Lir was in great sorrow when he heard this news, for then he understood well that his wife was trying to make an end of the four children. On the morrow he followed the road they had taken. As he went by the shores of Loch Darvra, his children saw his chariot and horses.

'A welcome to those horses,' said Finnola. 'By the sadness of them I think it is us they are following. Surely it is none other than Lir.'

At the edge of the lake, Lir heard swans calling to him in the voices of people.

'O Lir,' cried the swans, 'we are your own four children, destroyed out of jealousy by your wife, our mother's sister. There is no way to help us. No one in the world can change back our shape till the end of nine hundred years.'

When Lir and his people heard this, they gave three heavy groans of grief and sorrow and lament. That night, as they camped by the lake, the swans made them the sweet Irish music of the *shee*, and their hearts were eased a little. At dawn, Lir rose up to leave, and he laid this complaint on the quiet waters.

'O Finnola and handsome Conn,' he cried, 'O Aed and Fichra of the beautiful arms, I must leave though I am not ready. I lie down at night but I cannot sleep. To be parted from you torments my heart. I threw a cruel net about you, when I took Eva into my house. But how could I know what it would bring upon me?'

Then Lir went quickly to the house of Bodb Derg and told him what he knew. It was clear to the son of the Dagda that Lir spoke only the truth. Bodb sent for Eva and gave her hard words.

'This treachery of yours,' he said with anger, 'will be the worse for yourself in the end. What is the shape you hate the most?'

'The worst of it would be,' she said, 'to become a demon of the air.'

'And so you shall be,' said Bodb. Then touching her with his druid's wand he turned her immediately into a demon of the air. In that shape she rode way on the wind. She is in it yet, and will stay so till the end of life and time.

All the peoples of Ireland, the Tuatha De Danann and the Sons of Mile, used to be coming to the lake to hear the music of the swans. For there was never anything heard in Ireland to compare with that music. The men of Ireland gathered there every day, to be telling stories and talking with teachers and friends. And every night they listened to the sweet music of the *shee*. All who heard that music slept sound, free from the trouble and sickness that rest on mankind.

For three hundred years these meetings went on. Then on a certain day Finnola said to her brothers, 'Do you know our time here is almost spent? There is but one night left.'

And there was sorrow on the children of Lir, for they thought it better to be talking sweet Irish by the fair lake than to be swimming at Moyle on the cold north sea.

On the morrow they made ready to fly away.

'Farewell friends and kinsfolk,' called Finnola to the people. 'O farewell Bodb Derg, wisest of kings, and farewell our dear father, Lir of the White Field Hill. O most pleasant company, my grief it is not to see you again. We are banished to Moyle, of the tormented sea, for three hundred years, far from the dance of music and the talk of kin. It is a most sorrowful parting.'

Then airily they took flight to the Sea of Moyle, and those left behind in sadness, the people of Ireland, from this moment forbade for all time the killing of swans.

When the children of Lir came to their new home, they saw a wide coast filled with cold and storm. It was a bad dwelling-place for them. Often wind and gale drove them apart, and they struggled to meet again by the Rock of the Seals. Great storms, and the flash of lightning, and high-stepping waves scattered them to the ends of the ocean. Finnola, on the Rock of the Seals, waited often in fear for the calm day and rising sun to bring her dear brothers into safety, back under the feathers of her breast.

'O my brothers,' she would sigh, 'it was a foul night for us, and many others like this one are before us still.'

They lived there long, in the misery of the Moyle, till a night came such as they had never known before for frost and snow and wind and cold. They were on the Rock of the Seals and the water froze about them, and their feet and their feathers froze to the rock. They could not move at all. With great stirring, at last they tore themselves away, but they left feathers and the tips of the their wings and the skin of their feet stuck to the rock.

'Now our state is bad indeed,' said Finnola, 'for we cannot bear the salt water to touch our wounds. It will be the death of us. One daughter and three sons, surely it is a pity the way we are, torn from the ragged rocks, our only feast the salt water of the blue tide.'

Their feather grew again, and for a long time they went here and there, drifting on the mournful waters of the Sea of Moyle. Then one day, by chance, they came to the mouth of the Bann, in the north part of Ireland. On the shore-side, they saw bright-coloured horsemen, with white horses under them, riding the road from the southwest.

'What men are those?' they wondered. 'Surely they are from the Tuatha De Danann, or from the Sons of Mile. They have the look of our own people.'

The children of Lir swam close to the shore and called out in the voice of humans, and they mixed their talk with the troop of the horsemen. The chief men in this troop were two of the sons of Bodb Derg, that is to say Aed of the Quick Wits and Fergus the Chess Player, and they had riding with them a third of the warriors of the *shee*.

'What news,' said the children of Lir, 'of our people, of our father Lir, of the noble king?'

'They are well,' came the reply, 'in one place together, in your father's house at Shee Finnaha. There is no unhappiness on them, except for the lack of you yourselves, and not knowing what came of you after you left the Lake of the Oaks.'

Then Finnola answered with a heavy heart, 'That is not the way with us, for we have ageless misery on the tides of the sea. There is pleasure tonight in the house of Lir, with ale and wine for good company, but only a cold dwelling-place for his four poor children. Once we dressed in purple and drank the laughter-giving mead. Now the rock is our bed and feathers our bedclothes, and bitter water our only drink. The king's court used to ride after us to the Hill of Bodb. I remember the teaching of Manannan, the talk of the king on the pleasant ridge, the voice and sweet kisses of Angus. Now I waste my strength, to and fro without end, on the angry current of the Moyle.'

'There is no help for it,' cried the men of the Tuatha De Danann. 'We have no power to change you. But all will become well in the end of time.'

Then for the children of Lir their years were finished on the Sea of Moyle, and a new time of trial began on the western ocean, stark cold and gale-tossed between Erris and the Isle of Glora. Another three hundred years they had of it there. Then Finnola called her brothers gladly for the flight home.

Lightly they flew to Shee Finnaha. But the place was empty before their eyes, nothing in it but green hillocks and thickets of nettles, without house, without hearthstone, without fire.

'This is a wonder to me,' Finnola lamented, 'a broken house, without a chief, without women, without hounds for hunting. It was not thus in our father's day – no horns, no cups, no drinking. The stables are empty, the riders gone. Grass and bushes cover the ruins. The person is not living who would know us. Strange would we be to any visitor.'

The children of Lir stopped that night in the place of their father and their grandfather, and they sang the sweet sad music of the *shee*. In the morn, they rose up early and flew to the Isle of Glora, and all the birds of the land gathered around them at the Lake of the Birds. Each day, they went to feed to Iniskea and to Achill, to the western isles of Connacht and to the place where Donn, son of Mile, was drowned and buried. Then each night they returned to sleep on the Isle of Glora.

Now, there came a time when blessed Patrick and the faith of Christ arrived in Ireland, and Saint Kemoc went into the Isle of Glora. The first night he was there the children of Lir heard the voice of his bell ringing near them. They started up, and the brothers said, 'What is that weak, unpleasing voice we hear?'

''Tis the bell of Kemoc,' said Finnola, 'and through that bell we shall be free of our pain and misery.'

They listened to the bell till the matins were done, and then they began to sing the sweet sad music of the *shee*.

Kemoc heard their singing and went down to the lake. But he saw only four swans on the water.

'Is it you,' he said, 'that are the children of Lir?'

'Indeed we are,' they replied.

'Then I give thanks to God,' said he, 'since I came to this island for your sakes. Let you come to land now, and give me your trust, that you may do good deeds and depart from your sins.'

So they came to land and trusted Kemoc. He brought them to his own little place, and then he asked a good smith to make chains of bright silver. One he fixed between Aed and Finnola, and the other between Conn and Fichra. And the four of them gladdened his heart and his mind. The swans were content to rest in peace and had their troubles on the wide sea put behind them.

At that time, the king of Connacht was Largnen, son of Colman, and his wife was Decca, daughter of Finnin. And the joining of this pair was the coming together that Eva had spoken of long ago, when a prince of the North should marry a woman of the South. Now, the woman Decca heard talk of the wonderful swans, with their sadness and their music, and she had a great desire to have them. Her husband sent messengers to Kemoc to ask for the birds, but he would not give them up.

In anger Largnen himself went to the place of Kemoc. He grabbed hold of the swans, two birds in each hand, and pulled them from the little altar, to bring them to Decca. But no sooner had he touched them than their skins fell off, and what was in their place but three withered men and a wrinkled old woman with scant flesh or blood?

Then the king jumped with fright and instantly left that place. When he was gone, Finnola said to Kemoc, 'Come, holy man, baptize us now, for the time of our death is near, though it will be a sorrow for us all to part from each other. Make our grave here and lay Conn at my right side and Fichra at my left, and put Aed before my face in the compass of my arms.'

The children of Lir were baptized, and they died. They

were buried as Finnola had said, with Conn at her right side and Fichra at her left and Aed before her face. A stone was put over them, and their names were written in Ogham. That night, there was a wailing at their going, but their souls were already on the road into heaven.

MANAWYDAN, SON OF LLYR

There was a time when Manawydan looked about him, and on his companions, and he heaved a great sigh and felt much grief and longing within him.

'Alas, unhappy that I am,' he said to Pryderi, 'there is none save me without a place of my own.'

'Lord, be not so sad,' said Pryderi. 'You have never coveted land nor office. Not without reason are you called one of the Three Ungrasping Chieftains. But hear now what I have to say. Seven estates of Dyfed were left to me, and Rhiannon my mother is there. Her and the land both I will bestow on you. Had you no other land except those seven estates, yet would you be well pleased with yourself. And as for Rhiannon, who is more pleasant than she? In her youth there was none more beautiful, and even now her looks will still make you glad.'

Together they went to Arberth in Dyfed, and Rhiannon and Pryderi's wife Cigfa prepared a feast for their coming. Then Manawydan and Rhiannon began to sit together and talk. As they talked, his head and heart grew tender towards her.

'Pryderi,' he called out, 'I will keep to your offer.'

'What offer was that?' said Rhiannon.

'Lady,' replied Pryderi, 'I have bestowed you as wife upon Manawydan, son of Llyr.'

'I will abide by that,' said Rhiannon.

'And gladly will I too,' said Manawydan.

Before the feast ended he slept with her, and a great celebration began. After a time, as they were sitting in the midst of company, there was a mighty peal of thunder and a fall of mist so that none could see the other. After the mist every place was filled with light. But when they looked up, where before they had seen flocks and herds and houses, now they could see no manner of thing. Neither house nor beast nor smoke nor fire nor man nor dwelling was there. The court was empty, desolate, uninhabited. All their company was lost and gone save the four of them only, Manawydan and Pryderi and their wives.

'Alas, where is our court and company?' said Manawydan in wonder. So they looked in the hall and the bower and the sleeping-chamber, and not a soul was there. They looked in the cellar and the scullery and the kitchen, and all was desolation.

There was no help for it but to eat and hunt and take their pleasure. They wandered, each one, here and there in the land, but no person or house could they see, only wild beasts. They lived on the meat of the hunt and on fish and on the gifts of nature. They passed a year, and a second, and at last they grew weary.

'By our faith,' said Manawydan, 'we cannot live like this.' But they kindled fire and hunted and went on for another year.

One morning, Pryderi and Manawydan made ready their dogs for hunting. Soon the dogs drove a wild boar out of a thicket, and they bayed after it. They followed it close, pursuing it into a large fort, newly built, in a place where neither stonework nor building had been seen before. From the top of a mound the men looked and listened for the dogs, but they neither saw nor heard them.

'We never saw this fort here,' said Pryderi. 'Let us be warned not to go inside. Surely he who has put this spell on the land has also made this fort. But faith, I'll not lose my dogs.' And at once he ran into the fort.

In the middle of the floor he saw a marble fountain, with a golden bowl at its edge fastened to four chains that went up into the air without any ends in sight. Wondering at the beauty of the gold and the exceeding fine work of the bowl, Pryderi took hold of it. But his hands stuck to the bowl, and his feet to the marble slab below it. The power of speech was driven from his mouth, and thus he stood all dumb.

Manawydan waited outside till the close of day. He was afraid to enter, so he went away and told Rhiannon what had happened.

'You are a bad friend,' she said, 'but a good comrade have you lost.'

Then she went quickly to the fort, and finding the gate open she went in at once. When she saw Pryderi with his hands fast on the bowl, she laid hold to help him, and then she herself was stuck fast and unable to utter a word. In this way, they were rooted till nightfall, when once again there was a peel of thunder and a fall of mist, and the fort vanished and they too.

When Cigfa saw that her husband was gone and there was no one left to her but Manawydan, she cried that she might as well be dead. But Manawydan rebuked her.

'Have no fear of me,' he said. 'I give you my word that you will find no truer friend. Were I in the very flush of youth, still I would keep faith with Pryderi, and for your sake too I will keep it.' Then she was content and thanked him.

'But we cannot stay here,' he went on. 'We have lost our dogs and cannot hunt for food. Let us try some other place.'

As they made their way through Dyfed towards Arberth, Manawydan found that he had in the folds of his clothes some ears of wheat. He set up his dwelling in Arberth, in the place that had pleased him most when Rhiannon and Pryderi were with him. He fished and snared wild animals, and afterwards he began to till the ground and sow three fields of wheat. The wheat sprang up, the best in the world, and his crop thrived. No mortal had seen finer wheat.

In time the harvest was ripe and he thought, 'I'll reap it in the morning.' In the grey dawn he came with his sickle, but he found all the stalks naked, with the ears of the wheat broken off and carried away. And on the next morn, so it was with the second field.

'Who is doing this thing that ruins me,' said Manawydan, 'and ruins the country also?' That night he decided to keep watch over his third field.

Towards midnight he heard the greatest commotion in the world. He looked and saw a mighty host of mice, so many they seemed numberless. Mice were running up all the stalks of the wheat, biting off the ears and leaving the stalks naked. There was not a single stalk that had not a mouse on it.

In anger he rushed amid the mice. But it was like attacking a swarm of gnats or a flight of starlings. The mice divided and flowed and eddied about him like water. One, at least, he could see was heavy and dull with no fleetness of foot. So he caught that mouse and put it in his glove and tied up the mouth with string. When he returned home, he greeted Cigfa and stirred the evening fire and hung the glove by its string from a peg.

'What is there, my lord?' said she.

'A thief,' he replied, 'whom I caught red-handed.'

'But what kind of thief,' she asked, 'could you put in your glove?'

Then he told her the tale, how his crops had been laid waste by the mice. 'One only was I able to catch, and I will hang that mouse tomorrow.'

'My lord, you are right to be angry,' she said. 'Yet consider, is it seemly for a man of rank and dignity to hang such a little creature? Do not meddle with such nothingness. Let it go.'

'If I could have caught them,' said Manawydan, 'I would have hanged them all, else I would be shamed. But this one I will hang.'

'Do what you will,' she said. 'I only speak to keep you from discredit.'

On the morrow he took the mouse to Gorsedd Arberth. On the highest point he planted two sticks. While he was doing this he saw a reverend clerk coming towards him, dressed in old, poor, threadbare clothes. Now it was seven years since Manawydan had last set eyes on any human other than his three companions – and two of those were now gone from him.

'What kind of work are you doing here?' asked the man.

'Hanging a thief.'

'What kind of thief? I see a creature in your hand very like a mouse. Let it go. It ill becomes a man of your rank to touch such a thing.'

'I will not let it go,' said Manawydan. 'I caught it thieving, and I will execute on it the law of thieves.'

'My lord, lest a man of your rank should be seen in such work, I will give you a pound that I have taken in alms, if you will let the creature go.' But Manawydan refused, and away went the clerk.

Manawydan began to fix a crossbeam to the forks, and then he saw a priest on a horse approaching.

'A blessing on you,' called the priest. 'What work are you doing there?'

'Hanging a thief,' he answered.

'What thief is that, my lord?'

'A creature in the shape of a mouse. It has stolen from me, and the doom of a thief will I give it.'

'My lord, lest you be seen handling that lowly thing, I will redeem it for three pounds. Let it go.'

'Between me and God,' said Manawydan, 'I want no price for it, save what is its due. And that is to hang.' So away went the priest.

Then Manawydan put a noose of string around the neck of the mouse. But as he was drawing it up he saw a bishop with his followers and his loads and his baggage making towards him.

'My lord,' cried the bishop, 'is not that a mouse I see in your hand, that you are about to hang?'

'It is a mouse, and a thief also.'

'Why, man, let the silly thing go. I will redeem it for seven pounds, lest a man of such rank should be seen destroying a worthless creature.'

'By God, I will not let it go.'

'Yea, you shall let it go, and I will give you four and twenty pounds of ready money.'

'I will not, not for as much again.'

'Then I will give you all the horses you see on this plain, and also my own seven horses and the seven loads of baggage that go with them.'

'By heaven, I still say no.'

'Well,' said the bishop, 'name your price for that worthless mouse.'

'It is that Rhiannon and Pryderi be set free.'

'You shall have it.'

'Still the mouse dies.'

'What more then?'

'Let the charms and enchantments be removed from the seven estates of Dyfed. Also, I would know who this mouse is.'

'She is my wife,' said the bishop, 'and were it not so I would take no trouble to free her. I am Llwyd, son of Cil Coed. It was I who cast the enchantments over the seven estates of Dyfed, to avenge the trick that Pryderi played on Gwawl, son of Clud. Hearing that you dwelt in this land, my soldiers asked me to change them into mice that they might destroy your corn. That happened on the first and second nights. On the third night my wife and the ladies of her court also asked to become mice, and I did that too. But she was great with child, and heavy and slow, or else you would not have caught her. Now I will give you Pryderi and Rhiannon and remove the enchantment, if you will let her go.'

But Manawydan answered, 'I will not let her go.'

'Well, what more then?' said Llwyd.

'Never again put any spell on the seven estates of Dyfed.'

'Easily agreed.'

'Yet still your wife shall not be free.'

'What now?'

'Promise further that no more vengeance shall fall on Pryderi and Rhiannon, nor upon me.'

'Faith, that was a shrewd stroke, but you shall have it. But for that condition no end of harm would have lighted on your head. Now set her free.'

'One last thing. I shall not let her go till I see Pryderi and Rhiannon safe and well.'

'See,' said Llwyd, 'here they are coming.'

Then Manawydan rose up to greet his dear friends. He welcomed them in joy and they sat down to talk.

'Ah, my good lord,' cried Llwyd, 'do not play false with me. You have received what you asked. Now set my wife free.'

Manawydan took the noose from the neck of the mouse, and Llwyd touched her with his wand and changed her into the fairest young woman that any had seen.

'Look now on this wide land,' said Llwyd. 'See the houses and the courts and the people, they are now as fair as they ever were.'

So they all rose up and looked about. And they saw all the land inhabited and complete again, with all its herds and flocks and people and dwellings.

Then Manawydan said to Llwyd, 'What pains and servitude did you put on Pryderi and Rhiannon?'

'Pryderi,' he replied, 'had the weights of the gates of my court hung about his neck, and Rhiannon had about her neck the collars of the asses after they had carried the hay. That was the extent of their pain and imprisonment. But that story is ended now.'

THE DREAM OF
RHONABWY

There was a time when Rhonabwy was on a quest in Powys, and he arrived for lodgings at the house of Heilyn Goch. As he and his companions came towards the house they could see a black old hall with a straight gable-end, all smoke-grimed. Inside was a floor full of holes and bumps, so a man might hardly stand, and the floor was slippery with the stale and dung of cattle, mixed in with half-chewed branches of holly. Above the floor was a dusty platform of bare boards, and an old crone feeding a fire. Against the cold she threw on a lapful of husks, so that it was not easy for any man alive to endure the smoke in his nose. At the far end of the platform was a yellow ox skin, and good luck to the one of them who would get that to sleep on.

The crone greeted them rudely and they waited awhile for

the people of the house to return. Then there entered a wizened, bald old man with a little fuzz of red hair, and a skinny, blotched-faced woman with a bundle under her arm. And they too had no more than a cold welcome for the guests. The woman lit a meagre fire of sticks. For food, she brought them cheese and barley-bread and watered milk.

After they had eaten, a storm of wind and rain settled on the house, so that a man might hardly go out, even to relieve himself. The travellers were exceedingly weary from their journey. They drowsed and nodded, dozing without comfort in the smoke.

The resting place was covered with flea-ridden straw and the thick ends of the branches eaten by the oxen. A greyish, threadbare, flea-hopping blanket was spread on the straw, and over it was a coarse sheet in tatters, and a filthy pillow as hard as a stone. Here, sleep came heavily to Rhonabwy's two companions after the fleas and the lumps and the cold had gnawed at them. But Rhonabwy tossed about. He thought it would be less of a torture to rest on the yellow ox-skin of the platform. And there at last he slept.

As he slept, he was granted a vision. He and his companions were crossing the plain of Argyngroeg towards Rhyd-y-Groes on the Severn. Ahead of him he heard a commotion the like of which he had never heard before.

He saw a youth with yellow curly hair and a new-trimmed beard, riding a yellow horse, and his legs all in green. The tunic of the horseman was yellow brocade silk sewn with green thread, and on his thigh was a sword with a golden hilt in a scabbard of new leather with a clasp of gold and a deerskin thong. He had a mantle of yellow silk, and the fringes of this were green. And all these green colours were as green as the fronds of the fir-tree, and the yellow of it was as yellow as the flowers of the broom.

Rhonabwy and his companions fled from this large awesome figure, and the rider galloped after them. When the horse breathed out, the men fleeing grew distant from the rider, and when it breathed in they were drawn right up to the horse's chest. Then Rhonabwy and his friends asked for mercy.

'Gladly,' said the rider, 'let there be no fear upon you.'

'My good lord,' they replied, 'tell us who you are.'

'I will tell that. I am Iddawg, the Embroiler of Britain. And I will tell you the reason for that name. I was an envoy at the battle of Camlan, between Arthur and Medrawd his nephew. A bold young man was I then! I loved battle and I stirred up strife. When I was an envoy I changed fair words into ugly threats, so that Arthur and Medrawd would fight. Out of that was woven the battle of Camlan, and thus I was named Iddawg, the Embroiler of Britain. Even so, three nights before the end of the battle I was ashamed and I fled to do penance at Y Llech Las. Seven years I did penance, and then I was pardoned.'

After speaking together they all went on across the great plain as far as Rhyd-y-Groes on the Severn. A mile from the ford, on both sides of the road, they could see the tents and pavilions of a great host. From the bank of the river they saw Arthur seated on a flat island below. With Arthur were Bedwin the bishop and Gwarthegydd the counselor and a big auburn-haired youth. This young man had his sword in his hand, and about him was a tunic of pure black silk. His face was as white as ivory and his eyebrows were as black as jet. His wrist between his glove and his sleeve was whiter than the water-lily and thicker than the calf of a warrior's leg.

As they came up to Arthur, the king greeted them. 'God prosper you,' he said, 'but Iddawg, where did you find those little fellows?'

'I found them, lord,' said Iddawg, 'way up on the road.'

Arthur smiled, and Iddawg asked him, 'My lord, why do you laugh?'

'Nay, I am not laughing,' replied the king, 'but I feel it sad that men as mean as these now keep this Island, after men as fine as those that kept it before.'

While the king was talking, Iddawg said quietly into Rhonabwy's ear, 'Do you see the bright stone in the ring on the king's hand? It is a virtue of the ring that you shall remember all you see here tonight. Otherwise, not a whit of this would you recall.'

Then Rhonabwy looked about him and saw a troop of men coming to the ford. Every one of that troop, man and horse, was as red as blood. Each was like a pillar of fire mounting into the sky. And at the same time, another troop was coming to the ford, and their upper parts were as white as lilies and their lower parts as black as jet. The foremost rider spurred into the ford and made the water splash over Arthur, wetting him as wet as a man in the sea. Then swords were drawn and rebukes given and taken.

There was much riding to and fro, and soon many men at arms were gathered. Then a proud, handsome man came forward and said it was a marvel how a host so big was contained in a place so small. But he thought it a greater marvel that he should find here, at this very hour, those who had promissd to be in Baddon by midday, to fight against Osla Big Knife.

'Now you speak the truth,' said Arthur calmly. 'Come, let us go together.'

'Iddawg,' said Rhonabwy, 'who is he that dares to speak to Arthur in that way?'

'It is Caradawg Stout Arm, Arthur's counsellor and cousin, a man who may speak as bluntly as he wishes.'

Then Iddawg took Rhonabwy up behind him on the saddle and they set out with a great host towards Cefyn Digoll. As they passed over the river, Rhonabwy saw coming in one direction the warriors of Scandinavia, in white silk bordered with black, and in the other direction the men of Denmark, in black silk bordered with white.

Below Caer Faddon, as Iddawg and Rhonabwy joined the swelling ranks of this army of the Mighty, there was turmoil and disorder in the host. Then the call went out for Cadwr, Earl of Cornwall. He arose and took Arthur's sword in his hand, and the sword had the image of two serpents on it chased in gold. When the sword flashed, two flames of fire were seen in the mouths of the serpents, and the sight of it was dreadful and not easy to look upon. Men cast down their eyes and the tumult ceased.

Then Eiryn, Arthur's servant, advanced. He was a large,

rough-headed, ugly fellow, with a red moustache, and red hair standing up like pig's bristles. In front of Arthur he dismounted from his big red horse, which wore a parted mane, and took from his pack a golden chair and a cloak of ribbed silk. The cloak was spread on the ground, weighted by a golden apple at each corner, and the chair, big enough for three warriors, was placed on the cloak. Gwen was the name of that cloak. It was a magic cloak that made the wearer invisible.

Arthur sat on the chair in the middle of the cloak. Then he turned to Owen, son of Urien, who was standing beside him.

'Owen,' said Arthur, 'will you play at chess?'

'I will, my lord,' said Owen.

The red-headed servant set up the chessboard, gold pieces on a silver board. And they began to play.

As they bent over the game, a youth came from a white and red pavilion with a black serpent pictured on the top. Red, venomous eyes were in the serpent's head, and its tongue glowed like a flame. The blue-eyed youth had curly fair hair and a beard just sprouting. He wore a tunic of yellow silk, and greenish-yellow hose. His shoes were of speckled leather, with buckles of gold across the instep. A heavy triple-grooved sword with a gold hilt hung at his side in a scabbard of black leather.

This squire advanced and greeted Owen.

'My lord,' he said, 'is it with your leave that the king's young knights are harassing and molesting your ravens? If not, have the king call them off.'

'O king,' Owen said to Arthur, 'you hear what this squire says? If it please you, call them off my little ravens.'

'Play the game,' said Arthur. And the squire returned to his pavilion.

They finished that game and started another. In the middle of that game a ruddy, keen-eyed, well-built lad, with his beard shaved, came from a bright yellow pavilion with a red lion on top. He was dressed in yellow sown with red silk. His stockings were white buckram, and his shoes were of black leather. He pulled a huge sword from a sheath of red deer-skin, and he came to the place where they were playing chess. He saluted Owen.

'Is it your will,' he said, 'that the king's young knights should be wounding your ravens? Beseech the king to call them off.'

'My lord king,' said Owen, 'call them off.'

'Play the game,' said the king, and the squire went away.

That game was ended and another begun. Just as they were starting, they saw a spotted yellow pavilion, the largest ever seen, with the emblem of a golden eagle on it. A fair and graceful youth advanced from the pavilion, with a pale face and great hawk-like eyes. He held a standard flying from the end of a thick speckled spear, with the bright point newly sharpened. He rode in rage and passion at a quick canter to the place where the chess was being played.

'The best of the ravens are slain,' he shouted to Owen, 'and the others so wounded and hurt that not one of them can rise up on wings six feet from the ground.'

'My lord,' said Owen, 'call off your men.'

'Play the game,' said the king, 'if you will.'

Then Owen turned to the squire and said, 'Away with you. Where the battle is thickest raise high the standard, and let it be as God wills.'

So the squire raised the standard in the thickest part of the battle. As the standard was raised, so too the ravens rose into the air in rage and courage. They threw off their fear as they felt the wind in their wings. They recovered their magic power and strength, and they swooped down to earth on the men who had given them injury and loss. They struck the heads off some, and from others they plucked eyes or ears or arms. There was a thrashing and clamour in the air, and anguish and agony on the ground from wounded and dying men. In amazement at the great noise, Arthur and Owen looked up from the chess.

They saw coming towards them a rider in strange barbaric colours, vermilion and yellow and green and dapple-grey, and each part of him was in a colour different to another

71

part. He wore the armour of a distant land, and his helmet was crested with the emblem of a yellow-red leopard. Which was the worse to look on, the leopard of the helm or the man's fierce face? This horseman held a long spear and on its point were the blood and guts of the ravens.

'O king,' said this grim knight, 'the ravens are slaying your young men.'

Arthur looked at Owen and said, 'Call off your ravens.'

'My lord,' said Owen, 'play the game.'

They played on. Around them they could hear the howls of the men and the shrieks of the ravens as they dashed and tore at their enemy and let them fall in pieces to the ground.

Then out of this tumult rode a horseman in heavy green armour on a white horse. The coverings and trappings of the horse were pure black with fringes of yellow. On the rider's head was a helm with the crest of a golden lion, and a tongue of flame a foot-length came from the mouth of the lion. In his hand he had a blood-stained lance of ash-wood.

'My good lord,' he cried to Arthur, 'your young knights have been slain, those noble sons of the Island of Britain. Now who will defend the Island from this day forth?'

'Owen,' said Arthur, 'call off your ravens.'

'My lord,' he replied, 'play this game.'

That game ended and another began. As they played towards the end-game of the chess, out of the blood and turmoil came a large stern knight on a handsome black horse. His cloak was purple and his helmet was crested with a griffin. In a rage he galloped all hot and bloody to within a foot of Arthur.

'My lord,' he shouted, 'my warriors are dead and my army destroyed. It is the work of the ravens.'

Then Arthur took the golden pieces of the chessboard and crushed them till they were dust.

'Owen,' he said, 'tell your standard-bearer, Gwres, son of Rheged, to lower his banner.'

Therewith the standard was lowered and all was peace.

When the fighting was over, Osla Big Knife sent four and

twenty knights to King Arthur, to ask for a truce for a month and a fortnight.

Arthur summoned his council of chief men, and with him were Bedwin the bishop, and Gwarthegydd, son of Caw, and March, and Caradawg Stout Arm, and many other bold men. And while they talked bards came with the songs of their poems. All they sang was in praise of Arthur, but never a man could understand such rich and wonderful words except he be Cadyrieith the bard himself.

After this, twenty-four asses arrived with their loads of gold and silver, bringing tribute to Arthur from the Isles of Greece. The truce was granted to Osla Big Knife for a month and a fortnight, and the treasure brought by the asses was given to the bards, in reward for their songs.

Then Cei arose and said to the whole company, 'Whoever will follow Arthur, let him be with us tonight in Cornwall. As for the others, let them meet with Arthur at the end of the truce.'

At once, there was a swirl of men and horses, and a stamping and a shouting, and in the midst of this noise Rhonabwy awoke. He was stiff and cold on the yellow ox-skin, and he had slept for three nights and three days.

3

FABLES
AND
TALKING BEASTS

'Here's meat and music!' said the fox
as he ate the bagpipe.

FABLES

A fox caught a fine fat goose asleep by the side of a loch. As the goose was cackling and hissing, the fox taunted her.

'Weel now, cackle away,' said Rory, 'but if you had me in your mouth, as I have you, what would you be doing?'

'Why,' said the goose, 'that's an easy question. I'd fold my hands, shut my eyes, say a grace, and eat you.'

'Exactly,' said Rory.

He folded his hands, put on a solemn face, shut his eyes, and said grace. As he did so, the goose spread her wings and was off, halfway over the loch.

'I'll make a rule of this,' muttered Rory as he licked his dry lips, 'never in my life to say grace till after I feel the warm meat in my belly.'

A fox and a cock were talking one day.

'How many tricks can you do?' said the fox.

'I can do three,' said the cock. 'How about yourself?'

'At least three score and thirteen,' said the fox scornfully.

'Surely that's a great number. Tell me one.'

'Well, my grandfather taught me to shut one eye and give a great shout.'

''Tis nothing,' said the cock. 'I could do that myself.'

And the cock closed an eye and crowed fit to burst. But the eye he shut was the one next to the fox, so the fox grabbed him by the neck and was away with him.

But the good housewife saw her cock being carried away and cried out, 'Let go of that bird. He's mine.'

At this, the cock whispered to the fox, 'Tell her that this cock now belongs to you.'

The fox opened his mouth to speak and out dropped the cock. In a moment he had flown up to the roof of the house, with one eye shut, and crowing to beat the band.

A magpie had a nest in the holly-bush, but the fox robbed it and ate the young ones. So the magpie had no love for the fox.

One day when the fox had nothing to eat, he met the magpie.

'Fine day,' said she.

'Fine day,' said the fox, 'but I'm fasting.'

'No need for that,' said the magpie, 'you'll eat soon enough.'

Two girls were going to the turf bog with baskets on their heads. One had bread and butter in her basket, and the other had a load of curds. The magpie flew softly on top of one basket and threw down bread and butter, then she flew onto the other and threw down the curd. The fox gobbled it all up, as much as he could, and soon he had to lie down to ease his belly.

'Now I'm fit to burst,' groaned the fox, 'what will I do?'

'Rest you quietly there,' said the magpie. 'I'll steal some medicine from the doctor and give you a purge.'

But the magpie flew fast to the man who kept hounds.

'In such and such a place,' she said, 'you'll find a fox who has eaten too much and can't move. Fetch your hounds and kill him.'

The magpie flew back to the fox and said, 'The doctor himself is coming. He's got the medicine for you.'

It wasn't long before one of the hounds bayed, and the fox cocked an ear.

'Is it the hounds?' he cried.

'Just a small one chasing the sheep,' said she.

But the hounds came with a rush, snarling and snapping. As the fox shook himself in terror, the magpie called out, 'Here's your purge. Try it now.'

The fox shook and stretched and tried to run but it was no use. The hounds caught him and tore him to pieces. That's the purge he got.

The eagle and the wren were seeing who could fly the highest. The winner was to be king of the birds. The wren flew away first, straight up. But the eagle came by, soaring easily in great circles. The wren was tired, so as the eagle passed he settled himself softly on the eagle's broad back.

At last, the eagle was growing weary.

'Where are you, wren?' he cried.

'I'm here,' answered the wren, 'just a little above you.'

And so the wren won that match.

The old crow was teaching the young one and she said to him: 'If you see one coming, and a thin stick in his oxter with a broad end to it, flee. That will be a gun, and he'll mean to kill you. If you see one bending down to lift a pebble, flee. That will be a stone he means to throw at you. But if you see one coming fair, straight ahead, without stopping or stooping, with nothing in his oxter, don't stir. That one will not touch you.'

'But what,' said the young one, 'if the stone is in his pocket?'

'Oh no,' said the old crow, 'be off with you. I see you need no more instruction.'

There was a woman before now, and she bore a hen in the rocks by the shore.

When the hen grew big, she used to be going to the king's house every day to get something to give to her mother. One day the king saw her.

'Nasty little creature,' he said, 'what are you doing standing upon my door?'

'Well,' said the hen, 'I may be little, and even nasty, but I can do a thing your fine big queen cannot.'

'What is that?' said the king.

'I can spring from rafter to rafter, with the tongs and the pot-hook trailing after me.'

So the hen did it, and the queen tried it. The queen took a spring out of herself, and she cut the edge of her two shanks, and she fell and the brain went out of her.

The king had four queens but the hen put them all out with this trick.

'It would be better for you now,' said the hen, 'to marry my mother. She is a fine woman.'

'Away with you,' cried the king. 'You have caused me enough loss already, you nasty creature.'

'It is best for you to marry her,' the hen said again.

So the king sent down for the hen's mother and had a good look at her. And the mother had a good look at him. That was satisfactory, so she herself and the king were married.

It was a bitter cold evening and the Old Crow of Achill didn't know how he would last out the night. He flew here and there till he saw, at the top of the tallest tree, a big nest. It would be a grand place to spend the night.

In the nest he found a fledgling eagle whose mother was away looking for food. The Old Crow took hold of the fledgling, and carried it off, and killed it in the wood. Then he flew back and settled in the nest.

It wasn't long before the mother eagle returned with a lump of meat. Night had fallen. She heard a stirring in the nest and dropped the meat to what she thought was her fledgling. The Old Crow ate it up quickly. Then the eagle settled down on top of him. It was a cold night, a most bitter night, and the eagle rose up and jumped about to keep warm. Never, she complained, had there been a colder night.

The Old Crow of Achill was in a sweat the whole night, warm under the breast-feathers, but he feared that the eagle would see him at dawn and kill him. So as the eagle was hopping up and down, moaning about the cold, the Old Crow piped up.

'This last night was nothing much,' he said. 'Certainly there's been a colder one.'

'How do you know that,' said the eagle, 'and you barely a month out of the shell?'

'Old May Night,' said the Crow, 'that was certainly a colder night. If you don't believe me, see the old Blackbird of the Forge. She'll tell you.'

The eagle still didn't believe it, but she flew off to the forge and found the Blackbird standing on an iron rod.

'Last night,' said the eagle, 'was the coldest I've ever known. I spent it rising up and down to try to keep warm. But my chick, not a month out of the shell, told me at dawn that there had once been a colder night, and that you would know it.'

'Certainly,' said the Blackbird, 'last night was the coldest I've ever felt. I've been here since I was young. The iron rod I'm standing on was long and thick at the time. Once every seven years I rub my beak on it, and if I rub it once more it will break. I've been here that long, and I can tell you last night was the coldest yet. But why don't you ask the Bull in the Field, he will know.'

The eagle flew off and she never stopped till she came to the Bull. She told her story and asked the Bull if there had ever been a colder night.

'I've been here for thousands of years,' said the Bull. 'Each year my two horns fall off and go to make the fence around this great field. Now, only two are wanting to complete the

81

fence, that's how long I've been here. And last night was the coldest night I've known. But the Blind Salmon of Assaroe is older than I. Maybe he can help you.'

So the eagle flew far away and she didn't stop till she saw the Blind Salmon swimming in his usual river.

'Are you the Blind Salmon of Assaroe?' said the eagle.

'That I am,' said he.

'Did you feel the cold last night?'

'That I did.'

'Tell me, was there ever a colder night?'

'Certainly,' said the Blind Salmon, 'there was a night colder than last night. It was on Old May Night long ago. I was here in this river. It was so cold I was jumping up and down in the water. It was freezing so hard that, one time when I jumped, the water froze while I was in the air and I froze on top of the ice. I was as stiff as a log and helpless. Soon after daybreak who should be passing but the Old Crow of Achill? When he saw me stuck in the ice, down he flew and started to peck. He made a hole in the ice and pecked out my eye and ate it. Ever since I've been called the Blind Salmon of Assaroe. But look you here,' the Blind Salmon went on, 'don't you think it was the Old Crow of Achill, and not your fledgling, in your nest last night?'

'Ah, surely not,' cried the eagle.

'It was,' said the Blind Salmon. 'Only he would know about the Old May Night.'

The mother eagle sped home in a panic. But both her chick and the Old Crow were gone. Just as well for the Old Crow. If the eagle had caught him, it would have been the end of his old, old days.

THE BROWN BEAR OF
THE GREEN GLEN

There was once a king in Ireland who had a leash of
sons. John was the youngest one, and it was said that
he was not wise in the head. Then his father, this good
worldly king, lost the sight of his eyes and the strength of his
feet.

The two eldest brothers said they would seek three bottles
of water from the Green Isles, which were somewhere in the
heaps of the deep. So away went these two brothers. Then
the young fool said to himself that he would go also.

The first big town he reached, there he sees those black-
guards, his two brothers.

'Ho, my boys,' says the young one, 'is it thus you are?'

'With swiftness of foot,' said they, 'take yourself home, or
we will have your life.'

'Rest easy, lads. It is no wish of mine to stay with you.'

John went away on his journey till he came to a great desert of a wood. 'Oh ho,' he says to himself, 'it is not canny for me to walk this wood alone.' Night was coming now, and growing pretty thick. So John tied the crippled white horse that was under him to a root of a tree, and he went up in the top himself.

He was but a very short time in the tree when he saw a bear coming with a fiery cinder in his mouth.

'Come down, son of Ireland's king,' cried the bear.

'Indeed I will not. I'm thinking I am safer up here.'

'If you won't come down, I'll go up.'

'Are you, too, taking me for a fool?' said John. 'A shambling shaggy creature like you climbing a tree!' But the bear fell at once to climb the tree.

'Lord, you can do it?' said John. 'Whoa there, keep back from the trunk and I'll go down to talk to you.'

John climbed down, and they came to chatting. Then the bear asked him if he was hungry.

'Weel, by your leave,' said John, 'I am a little at this very same time.'

• The bear made a wonderful watchful turnabout and caught a roebuck.

'Now, son of Ireland's king,' said he, 'is it boiled or raw that you like your share of the meat?'

'The sort of meat I'm used to,' replied John, 'would be kind of boiled.'

John got his share and when they had eaten the bear said, 'Lie down between my paws and you'll have no cause to fear till morning.'

Early next morning the bear roused John.

'It is time,' said the bear, 'to be on the soles of your feet. 'Tis a long journey, the best part of two hundred miles. But tell me, John, are you a good horseman?'

'There are worse than me,' said he.

'Then you had best get on top of me.'

He did that. But at the bear's very first leap John was flat on the earth again.

'Fie, fie,' cried John. But he struggled back on top and got a grim grip with his teeth and his nails. He was fastened to the bear in this way till they went the two hundred miles and reached a giant's house.

'Now John,' said the bear, 'you shall pass the night in this giant's house. You'll find him mighty grumpy, but say that it was the brown bear of the green glen that set you here for the night, and don't you be afraid that you'll not get a share of food and comfort.'

John went into the house, and the giant gave him a greeting.

'Son of Ireland's king,' he said, 'your coming was in the prophecy. If I didn't get your father, I have got the son. Shall I put you in the earth with my feet, or in the sky with my breath?'

'You'll do neither,' replied John, 'for it is the brown bear of the green glen that sent me.'

So that changed the tune of the giant. 'Come in,' said he, 'come in, and you shall be well taken to this night.'

And that was true, for John got meat and drink without stint, and good rest.

In the morning John and the bear went on, day after day, till they came to a second, and then a third giant.

'Now,' said the brown bear of the third one, 'I've little acquaintance with this fellow, but you'll not be long in his house before you must wrestle with him. If he is too hard on your back, you must say, "If I had the brown bear of the green glen here, that would be your master."'

Almost as soon as John went in that house, he and the giant got to grips. As they wrestled, they made a boggy bog of the rocky rock. In the hardest places they would sink to their knees, and in the softest up to their thighs, and they brought gushes of spring water from the face of the rock.

The giant gave John many a sore wrench so that at last he cried out, 'Fie, fie, if I had the brown bear of the green glen here, your leap would not be so hearty.'

No sooner had he spoken the words than the worthy bear was at his side.

'Ah, yes,' said the giant, 'now I know your business better than you do yourself, O son of Ireland's king.'

Then the giant ordered his shepherd to kill and bring home the best wether on the hill, and to throw the carcass before the great door.

'Now, John,' said the giant, 'an eagle will come to settle on this carcass. There is a wart on the ear of this eagle which you must cut off. But not a drop of blood must you spill.'

The eagle swooped down, and she was not long eating when John gave her such a close stroke of the sword that the wart was cut off without the least drop of blood. The eagle lifted her head from the carcass and put her sharp eye on John.

'Ride on the root of my wings,' said she, 'for I know your business better than you do yourself.'

Away they went on swift wings over land and sea, till they delved into the heaps of the deep where the Green Isles were.

'Quick John,' said the eagle, 'the black dogs are away. Fill your three bottles with water.'

As John was filling the bottles from the well, he saw a pretty little house, and he thought he would go in and take a look. In the first chamber he saw a full bottle. He filled a glass and drank, and it tasted good. But the bottle was still as full as before.

'I'll take this along with me,' he thought, and he added the strange bottle to his three bottles of water.

He went into another chamber and saw a loaf. He cut a slice, but the loaf was as whole as before. 'A man would be a fool to leave that,' said John, and he tucked it under his arm. In the next chamber, the same thing happened with a great round of cheese. In the last chamber he saw a young woman lying in the bed, and she was the prettiest little jewel of a girl you could ever find.

'It would be a great pity not to kiss your sweet lips, my love,' said John. And so he did.

John left the house and returned to the eagle. He jumped up between her wings and they flew over the sea back to the house of the big giant. There were some visitors in the house and the giant was giving them a great feast of meat and drink.

'Weel, John,' the giant welcomed him, 'was there ever such fine drink as this in your father's house?'

'Foo, my bold fellow,' said John, 'that's nothing. I have a drink here that is more rare than your drink and than my father's drink as well.'

Then he gave the giant a dram from his bottle, which stayed as full as before.

'Grand stuff indeed,' said the giant. 'For that, I'll give you myself two hundred notes, a bridle and a saddle, and all for that little bottle.'

'It's a bargain,' said John, 'but on this condition: you must give the bottle to the first sweetheart I had, if ever she comes this way.'

So it was agreed. And to make a long story short, John went and left the loaf and the cheese with the other two giants, under the same condition, that his first sweetheart should get them if she came that way.

At the end of these travels John went home to his father's big town in Ireland, and he saw his brothers – those black-guards! – as he had left them.

'You'd best come with me, lads,' says he, 'for I've got a dress of cloth and a bridle and a saddle for each of you.'

They went with him gladly, but as they approached their father's house they thought they had better kill him. So they set about him to do it. They left him for dead and threw the body behind a dike. Then they took his three bottles of water and home they went.

After some hours John came slowly to his wits, for he was not quite killed. He heard a cart coming down the road, clanking a load of rusty iron, and he called out, 'Whatever Christian man is there, O let him help me.'

His father's smith was the driver of the cart. He came to help John, not knowing who he was, so he picked him up and threw him among the old iron, to take him to town. As the cart jogged and jigged on the bumps, the rust went into John's every wound till he was scarred and blotched and rough-skinned and bald.

Meanwhile, at the pretty little house in the Green Isles,

the little jewel of a girl that John had left grew pale and heavy. In three quarters of a year, she gave birth to a fine baby lad.

'Lord help me,' says she, 'but how did I find this?'

'Fie, fie,' said the hen-wife, 'don't be worrying about that. Here's a bird for you. As soon as he sees the father of your son, the bird will hop on top of his head.'

Then the folk of the Green Isles were gathered from end to end, and all the people were put in the back door and out at the front. But the bird never stirred, and the father was not found. So the pretty little jewel said she would wander through the world altogether, till she found the father of her babe.

In a while of travelling she came to the house of the big giant and saw the bottle taken from her own home. 'Ah well,' she cried, 'who gave you this bottle?'

'Young John it was,' replied the giant, 'son of Ireland's king, that left it.'

'The bottle is mine,' she said, and she took it away.

In like manner she came to the houses of the other two giants, and she found and took away the loaf and the cheese. Then she journeyed some more and came at last to the house of the king of Ireland.

For her sake, five-fifths of the folk of Ireland were gathered, and the nobles of the land also. One by one, they were put in at the back door and out at the front, yet the bird did not stir.

'Is there any one other,' she asked, 'or any at all in Ireland who has not been here?'

They thought and they thought, and then the smith remembered.

'There is a bald, rough-skinned, ugly lump of a servant in my smithy,' he said, 'but surely he cannot be . . . '

'Rough or not rough,' she replied, 'bide no time but send him here.'

The servant was summoned, and no sooner did the bird see the head of this uncouth fellow than he took to flight and landed on the bald top. So it was made known that this lad was John and the father of her babe, and then she caught the dear man and kissed him.

'But John,' said the great king of Ireland, 'was it really you that fetched the three bottles of water that cured me?'

'Indeed, 'twas I.'

'Weel, then, what's to be done with your two brothers?'

'The very same thing,' said John, 'that they tried to do to me.'

In a moment, that same was done. And that was the end of those blackguards.

Then John married the pretty little jewel, who was the daughter of the king of the Green Isles. They made a great rich wedding that lasted seven years and seven days. And for all that time you could see the gold crushed from the soles of their feet to the tips of their fingers – yes, for the length of seven years and seven days.

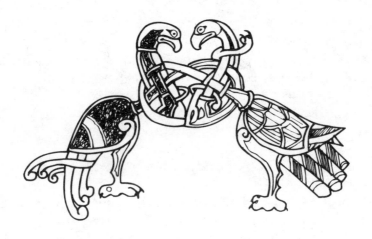

THE BATTLE
OF THE BIRDS

On this day of all the days, the creatures and the birds were gathering for battle. The son of the king of Tethertown wanted to see how the battle went. But it was over before he arrived, except for one fight between a great black raven and a snake. The victory seemed to be going to the snake, so the king's son lent a hand to the raven, and at last the raven took the head off the snake with one mighty blow.

The raven puffed out his cheeks and had a look at the dead snake. Then he said to the youth, 'For your kindness to me this day, I will give you a sight. Come up now on the root of my two wings.'

So the king's son mounted upon the raven who flew away with him over seven bens, and seven glens, and seven mountain moors.

'Now,' said the raven, 'do you see that house yonder? It is a sister of mine who makes her dwelling in it, and I'll go bail that you are welcome there. If she asks you, Were you at the battle of the birds? say that you were. And if she asks, Did you see my likeness? say that you saw it. But be sure that you meet me here in this place tomorrow morning.'

Indeed, the king's son got good and right good treatment this night, with meat of each meat, drink of each drink, warm water to his feet, and a soft bed for his limbs.

Next day, they again flew over seven bens, and seven glens, and seven mountain moors, and the king's son had the grandest entertainment as before. But on the third morning, instead of the raven to meet him, what should he find but the handsomest lad he ever saw, with a bundle in his hand.

'Ho, laddie,' said the king's son, 'has a big black raven been seen hereabouts?'

'Never again,' said the young man, 'will you see that raven, for I am that bird. I was put under spells, and it was you and our meeting that loosed me. For that you are getting this bundle. Now, turn back on the self-same steps you took before, and you will lie a night in each of the houses you saw on your way out. But do not let open the bundle till you are in the place your heart would like most for dwelling.'

The king's son turned about and put his face towards his father's house. On his way, he got lodgings from the raven's sisters, just as before. As he came near to his father's house, going through a close wood, it seemed to him that the bundle was growing heavy. He thought he would see what was in it.

He loosed the bundle and sprang back, and he was not without astonishment himself. In a twinkling he saw the very finest place that ever was. A great castle, and an orchard about the castle, in which was every kind of fruit and herb.

Then he was in wonder and regret, for it was not in his power to put it all back in his bundle. Yet he would rather

91

have it that this grand estate would be in the pretty green hollow by his father's house. While he was thinking this, at a glance he saw a big giant coming towards him.

'Bad is this place where you've built your house, king's son,' said the giant.

'Truly, it is not here that I would wish it,' said he, 'but here it is by mishap.'

'What reward would you give if I put it all back in the bundle?'

'What would you ask?'

'Give me your first-born son,' said the giant, 'when he is seven years old.'

'If I have a son,' replied the king's son, 'you shall have him.'

In a twinkling all was returned to the bundle, the fruit and the herbs and the orchard and the castle, as they had been before.

'Now,' said the giant, 'take your own road and I will take mine. But mind your promise. And though you forget, I will remember.'

In a few more days the king's son reached the place he liked best. He loosed the bundle, and at once the castle and the gardens were planted there, as grand as ever before. The king's son opened the castle door and in front of him was the most beautiful maiden he had ever seen.

'Advance, king's son,' said the pretty maid, 'all is in order for you. Will you marry me, this very night?'

'I am the man that is willing,' said he. And that same night they married.

In seven years and a day, who is seen coming to the castle door but the big giant. Then the king's son minded his promise, but till that moment he had told nothing to his wife.

'Turn out your son,' roared the giant, 'mind your promise.'

'You shall have him,' said the king's son, 'but first let his mother put him in order for the journey.'

Quickly the wife was told of the matter, so that she might dress the cook's son as her own and take him by the hand to the giant. Away they went, but the giant had not gone far when he put a rod in the hand of the little laddie and said, 'If your daddie had that rod, what would he do with it?'

'Why, he'd beat the dogs and the cats, if they would be going near the king's meat.'

'You're the cook's son,' cried the giant, and he grabbed the little fellow by the ankles and dashed his brains against a rock.

Then the giant returned to the castle in a rage.

'Turn out your son,' he roared, 'or the highest stone of this castle will be the lowest.'

'Try the trick yet once more,' pleaded the wife. 'The butler's son is of an age with our little laddie.'

So she dressed the butler's son and gave him by the hand to the giant. They had not gone far when the giant put a rod in the wee lad's hand and said, 'What would your daddie do with this?'

'Why, he'd beat the dogs and cats that came among the bottles and the glasses.'

'You're the butler's son,' said the giant, and he dashed him on the rocks too.

Now the giant returned to the castle in a very great rage, and the earth shook under the soles of his feet, and the tops of the towers trembled.

'Out with your son,' he roared, 'or in a twinkling the topmost stone will be the lowest.'

Then it needs must be that they give the right lad to the giant.

The giant took him home and reared him as his son. After a time, on a day when the lad was grown and the giant was away from home, the little fellow heard the sweetest music coming from a wee room at the top of the house. He glanced in and saw the prettiest face ever seen. She beckoned him and told him to be sure to be at the same place about the dead of midnight.

It was the giant's daughter to whom he made this promise, and sure enough at midnight she was at his side.

'Tomorrow,' said the girl, 'you will have the choice of my

own two sisters to marry. Choose neither, but take me. I am promised to the son of the king of the Green City, but he does not please me.'

On the morrow, the giant gathered his family together and said, 'Now, prince of Tethertown,' – for by this time, the lad's father had himself become king – 'you will not lose by living with me. Choose between my two eldest daughters for wife, and she shall go home with you after the wedding.'

'It's a good choice,' replied the youth, 'but better for me is this pretty little one. Give me her and I will take you at your word.'

Then the giant was angry and said, 'These three things you must do before you get that one: first, which I'll tell you now, there is the dung of my hundred cattle in the byre, that has not been cleansed for seven years. I am going from home this day. If by tonight the byre is not so clean that a golden apple will run undirtied from end to end, 'tis not my daughter you'll get, but it is a drink of your own blood that you'll give me for my thirst.'

The lad began cleaning the byre but he might as well have tried to bale the great ocean. At midday, when the sweat of effort was blinding him, the youngest daughter came to him.

'You are being punished, prince of Tethertown,' said she.

'Aye, that I am,' he replied.

'Come over, and lay down your weariness.'

'For that, death is waiting.'

But he was so tired he sat down beside her and fell asleep at once. When he awoke, the girl was not to be seen, but the byre was scrubbed so clean that a golden apple might run unsullied end to end. Then in came the giant at the end of the day.

'Have you cleaned the byre, king's son?' he said.

'It is clean,' he replied.

'Then someone else did it,' cried the giant in anger. 'But if you think you are so sprightly, this is what I have for you tomorrow. By this same time of day you must have thatched this byre with the feathers of birds so that no two feathers are of one colour.'

Next day, the lad was up before the sun, and he was out with bow and quiver in his hand. He wandered the moors but the birds were not easy to catch. Round and about he went till the sweat was blinding him. Then at midday, who should arrive but the giant's youngest daughter.

'You are wearying yourself, king's son,' said she.

'That I am,' he replied, 'but so far only two blackbirds have I caught, and both are of one colour.'

'Come over and lay your weary head on this pretty hillock.'

'I am right willing,' said he. He sat beside her, for he thought she might help him again, and very soon he was asleep.

When he awoke, the girl was gone and the byre was thatched in a multitude of coloured feathers. The giant saw it, and again he did not believe that the young lad had done it.

'Now,' said the giant, 'another task is this: down below is a fir-tree beside the loch, with a magpie's nest at the very top. Five eggs are in the nest. I must have them for my breakfast, and not one burst or broken.'

At first light, the young man went to look for the tree, and it was not hard to find. From root to first branch was five hundred feet. And the trunk was so stout he could get no grip on it. As he was going round and round, again the girl arrived.

'You are losing the skin of your hands and feet,' said she.

'Aye, that I am,' he said. 'I'm no sooner up than I'm down again.'

'No time to stop now,' she said. Then she thrust finger after finger into the tree till she had made a ladder for him to go up to the nest.

'Make haste now,' she called as he reached for the eggs, 'for my father's breath is burning my back.'

He slithered down, but in their hurry to be away, she left one little finger in the top of the tree.

'Haste you home with the eggs as quick as you can,' she cried, 'for your tasks are done. Tonight you will choose between us again, but I and my sisters will look exactly alike

95

in the same kind of dresses. So when my father says, "Go to your bride," look for the hand without a little finger.'

Then all went well. The lad gave the eggs to the giant, and he picked out the pretty girl with the missing finger, and so the giant agreed that there should be a wedding.

And it *was* a wedding! Giants and gentlemen and the son of the king of the Green City were there, and the dancing began, and that *was* a dance. The giant's house was shaking from top to bottom. At the end of the feast, the giant said, 'Go to rest, king's son, and take your wife with you. You have aimed well to find her. But there's no knowing, we may meet you yet another way.'

As they went to the chamber at the top of the stairs, the bride said to her husband, 'Sleep not, or else you die. Quick, quick, we must fly away before my father kills you.'

Out they went, as secret as moles, and untied the blue-grey filly in the stables. As they got ready to mount, the girl stopped for a moment.

'Wait a little,' she said, 'I've a trick to put in the path of the old fellow.'

So back she stole and cut an apple in nine pieces. Two shares she put at the head of the bed, two at the foot, two at the kitchen door, two at the big front door, and one outside the house.

After a while the giant awoke and called out, 'Are you a-bed and asleep, my pretty young ones?'

'Not yet,' answered the apple at the head of the bed.

Again and again he called, one time after another, and the apples answered in turn to the big front door.

'You are going far from me now,' cried the giant.

'Not so,' replied the apple outside.

'Yes, you're flying away,' said the giant. He jumped to his feet and ran to the bridal bed, but it was cold, cold, and empty.

'I am tripped by my own daughter's tricks,' he muttered. 'But here's off and after them!'

Wife and husband fled all night, but in the mouth of the day the girl felt her father's breath burning her back.

'Put your hand quick,' she told her husband, 'in the ear of our filly. Whatever you find, throw it behind us.'

He found a twig of sloe-tree and threw it. In the twinkle of an eye there rose up twenty miles of blackthorn wood, so thick that scarce a weasel might go through. The giant rushed into it headlong, and the thorns fleeced all his head and his neck.

'Here as before,' he grumbled, 'my own daughter's tricks. But if I had my big axe and wood-knife, I'd make short work of the way through.'

Home he went for his axe and his knife. He was not long on his journey, and he was a bonny lad to put some weight behind the big axe. Very soon he had cleared a path through the thorns. Then on he went at a mighty brisk clip till in the heat of the day his daughter once more felt her father's breath burning her back.

'Reach again in the filly's ear,' she said, 'and throw behind whatever you find.'

He found a speck of grey stone and tossed it behind, and in a twinkling there rose up, broad and high, twenty miles of grim grey rock. The giant came full pelt, but past the rock he could not go.

'The tricks of my daughter,' he groaned, 'are the hardest things that ever I met. But with my crowbar and pickaxe I'll not be long cleaving that rock.'

There was no help but that he must get them. And when he did, he was the bonny lad to split those stones. Then on he raced, and at the closing of the day, again his daughter felt his breath burning her back.

This time, the young king's son plucked a bladder of water from the filly's ear and threw it behind. At once, there grew a freshwater loch, twenty miles in length and twenty in breadth. The giant rushed on with all speed, and before he could stop he was halfway over the water. Then his legs thrashed the water and down he went, and he rode no more.

Next day, the bride and the husband came in sight of his father's house.

'Go you in,' said she, 'and tell them that you have the like of me. But remember this: let neither man nor creature kiss you. If you do, your eyes will forget that they ever saw me.'

As he went in everyone he met gave him welcome and luck, but he charged them, and his father and mother also, not to kiss him. But as mishap would have it, an old greyhound had such joy to see him that she sprang up and licked his face. After that he forgot entirely the giant's daughter.

He had left her sitting by a well in the wood, but he did not return to her again. In the mouth of the night she climbed into an oak for fear of the wild and lay in the fork of the tree. In the morn, a shoemaker that lived near the well sent his wife for a pitcher of water. As the wife looked in the well, she saw the reflection of the girl above in the tree. The woman was so surprised – she took the shadow on the water for her own and never had she looked so beautiful – that she dropped and broke the pitcher and went home.

'Wife, where's the water?' said the shoemaker.

But his wife had turned mighty proud and she answered, 'Shambling old fool, get it yourself. Too long have I been your slave for wood and water.'

'Woman, have you gone mad?' he cried. 'Well then, daughter, go quickly and get me a drink.'

His daughter went to the well, and it happened to her as it had to the mother. Never before had she looked so pretty and loveable, so she took herself home.

'Up with the drink,' said her father.

'Leather-stinking, homespun oaf,' she replied, 'do you think I'm nothing but your slave?'

'These women have taken a turn in the head,' the shoemaker thought, and away he went to the well himself. But when he saw the reflection in the water he had the wit to know what had happened. He looked up in the tree and saw the prettiest lass ever seen.

'Your perch is shaky,' he called to her, 'but your face is fair. Come down and I'll take you into my own house. I've only a little hut, but you'll get a decent share of all that goes.'

She went with him to the house, and at the end of a day or two there came a leash of young gentlemen lads to the shoemaker. The king's son had come home, and he was going to marry, and they needed new shoes for the wedding. Then the gentlemen lads saw the new girl in the house, and if they gave her one look they gave her two more, so pretty was she.

'Certainly, it is you that has the pretty daughter,' they said to the shoemaker.

'Aye, pretty she is,' said the shoemaker, 'but she's no daughter of mine.'

'By St Nail,' said one lad, 'I'd give a hundred pound to marry her!' And the other lads said the very same.

'Tell her this night what we have said,' they told the shoemaker, 'and send us word on the morrow.'

The girl had heard the sound of the talk, and after the lads had gone the shoemaker told her the drift of it.

'Go after them,' she said, 'I'll marry the one with the best purse.'

So the richest lad was called back and gave the shoemaker a hundred pound. After this, the girl and the lad went to rest. As the girl lay down she sent the lad for a tumbler of water. He took the tumbler from the board, but out of that grip he could not come, and he stood the long night with the glass in his hand.

'Ho, laddie,' she called, 'why will you not lie down?' But he stood like a stone till break of day.

Next morn, she asked the shoemaker to take away this lubberly boy. So this wooer went in a froth of puzzlement, and he did not tell his two companions how it had fared with him.

Then the second chap came and tried his luck with the pretty lady. They too went to rest, and she said to him, 'Look to the latch, if it's fastened on the door.' Well, the latch caught hold of his hand, and there he was till the break of day.

He was sent away in shame and disgrace, and it was the turn of the third lad. This time, the youth was rooted to the floor. In the morn he took his soles out of that house, and he was not seen looking behind him.

'Take the purses of gold that the foolish lads left,' said the girl to the shoemaker, 'for I have no need of them. They will better you, and I am no worse for your kindness.'

After a day and a day the shoemaker had the new shoes ready, and that was the very day of the marriage. As he made up his bundle to go to the court, the girl said to him wistfully, 'Such a day! How I would like to see this king's son before he marries.'

'Come with me,' said the shoemaker. 'The servants of the king know me well, and you shall get a sight of the king's son and all the company.'

When the gentlefolk saw a new pretty girl suddenly among them, they took her to the wedding-chamber and filled for her a glass of wine. She made as if to drink, and then a flame rose from the glass, and a golden pigeon and a silver pigeon flew out.

Then three grains of barley fell on the floor. The silver pigeon swooped down and ate them.

'If you had kept in mind,' said the golden pigeon, 'that I cleared the giant's byre, you would not eat that without giving me my share.'

Three more grains of barley fell, and the silver pigeon again ate them.

'If you had kept in mind,' said the golden bird, 'that I thatched the byre, you would not eat those without giving me my share.'

Another three grains fell, and the silver pigeon had them also.

'If you had kept in mind,' said the golden bird, 'the magpie's nest, you would give me my share. I lost my little finger then, and I lack it still.'

Then the pretty girl held out towards the king's son her hand without a finger, and he remembered at once who she was.

He sprang to where she was, and kissed her from hand to mouth. They called for the priest and they were married a second time, to make the matter sure. And that is where we leave them.

4

THE HERO-DEEDS OF CUCHULAIN

Here am I – no easy task –
Holding Ireland's men at bay.
My foot never turned in flight
From single man or ranks of foe.

Pillow-Talk

Once, when the royal bed was spread out at the fort of Cruachan in Connacht, Ailill and Maeve spoke together with their heads upon the pillow.

'True is the saying,' said Ailill, 'that it is well for a woman to be a rich man's wife.'

'True indeed,' said his wife, 'but what's in your mind?'

'It comes to my thought,' said Ailill, 'that you are better off today than when I married you.'

'I had wealth enough before you,' said she.

'Not so much, but only women's things, and enemies about you running off with spoil and booty.'

'Not at all,' said Maeve. 'My father, Eochaid the Steadfast, the High-king of Ireland, had six daughters and I was the best of them. I was great-hearted and generous and bold in battle. Fifteen hundred soldiers were in my pay, all mercenaries, and the same number of freeborn Irish followed me. I was my own woman, Maeve of Cruachan, ruler of this province given me by my father. Towards me the great men came wooing, from Leinster and from Tara. From Ulster also messengers came, from Conchobor and from Little Eochaid, and I would not go with them. For I asked a strange bride-gift, never before asked of a man of Ireland, namely, a husband without meanness, without jealousy, without fear.

'I am great in largesse and gift-giving, and if my husband were mean it would not be fitting to be together. I am strong in battle and victorious, and my courage would be reproached by a timid man, who should at least be of equal spirit. A jealous man would be wrong too, for I had lovers enough waiting in one another's shadow. So I found the man I wanted. It was yourself, Ailill, Rus Ruad's son from Leinster, not mean, not jealous, and no sluggard. I brought you gifts worthy of a noble bride: clothing for a dozen men, a chariot worth thrice seven bondmaids, the breadth of your face in red gold, the weight of your left arm in white bronze. Whoever brings shame and confusion upon you, the compensation is mine, for you are a kept man.'

'Not so,' said Ailill, 'for though my brothers are elder, and I let them govern, they are no better than I. I never heard of a province ruled by a woman except this one. So I came to the kingship here, following after my mother, Magach's daughter. And who better for my queen than yourself, daughter of the High-king of Ireland?'

'It may be so,' said Maeve, 'but my fortune is greater than yours.'

'I marvel at that,' he replied, 'for I know very well that none has more property or riches than I have.'

Then the poorest of their things were brought out to them, to judge who was the richer: their pails and cans and tubs and iron pots, their jugs and basins and eared pitchers. Then the gold treasure was brought out, bracelets and necklaces and rings for fingers and thumbs, and after that their garments and cloth, purple and blue and black and green and yellow, vari-coloured also, and grey, dun, mottled, brindled.

Their flocks were taken from the fields to be counted and

reckoned, and they were found to be equal. And Maeve's ram was no better than the ram of Ailill. Then from pasture and paddock came herds of horses, and Maeve had a match for Ailill's stallion. Great droves of pigs were gathered from the woods and glens and waste places, and one boar was as fine as another. The cattle were measured and compared, and the herds were the same in number and size.

But the great bull Finnbennach, the White-horned, had moved from the queen's herd to Ailill's, refusing to belong to a woman. Without a great bull, Maeve felt the heart go out of her, as if she owned not a pennyworth.

She sent for her messenger and said, 'Answer truly, Mac Roth, is there a match for this bull in any province of Ireland?'

'That there is,' said Mac Roth, 'a great and better one, at Cooley in Ulster, at the house of Daire, son of Fiachna. The Brown Bull of Cooley it is called.'

'Go, Mac Roth,' said Maeve, 'ask of Daire a year's loan of the Brown Bull. Let the payment be fifty heifers. And say further, Mac Roth, if the folk of the border object to the lending of their brown jewel, let Daire himself bring the bull and he shall have these gifts: a piece of the Plain of Ai equal to his own land, a chariot worth thrice seven bondmaids, and my own friendly body in bed.'

Away went Mac Roth to Ulster with this message. And Daire was so pleased with the offer that he burst the seams of his mattress for joy.

'On my heart and mind, to the devil with the wishes of Ulstermen!' he cried. 'My Brown Bull, my sweetheart, my treasure, shall go to Maeve and Ailill in the land of Connacht.'

Then there was good eating and drinking for all among the rushes and the straw, and soon the wits went awry with the drink.

''Tis true what I say,' said one of the men from Connacht, 'a good fellow we have here, this man of the house.'

'Certainly, a good man,' said another.

'None better in Ulster.'

'Nay, not so. The king Conchobor is a better man, and it's no shame to be his follower. Yet is it not a grand thing that Daire will give us the Brown Bull of Cooley? It would take the four provinces of Ireland to carry off that bull from Ulster.'

'What are you saying?' cried another. 'May your mouth gush blood! We would take the bull anyway, with or without permission.'

When he heard this, Daire's servant dashed down the dishes without grace or good word and went straight to his master.

'Was it you,' he said, 'that gave our treasure, the Brown Bull, to the messengers from Connacht?'

'Certainly, I did that,' said Daire.

'Was that a noble thing to do? It is true, then, what they say: they would have taken the bull by force, by your leave or not.'

'By all the gods, not so,' said Daire. 'I'll make the choice, fair or foul.'

So they went tumbling to bed, and in the morning the messenger of Connacht came to Daire's house.

'Tell us, noble sir,' said they, 'where the Brown Bull is.'

'I will not,' replied Daire. 'It is not in me to murder messengers or travellers, otherwise not one of you would leave here alive.'

'How so?' said Mac Roth.

'I have good cause for it. I hear say that I must give up the bull, or else the army of Ailill and Maeve, and the cunning of Fergus, will force me to it.'

'That speech,' said Mac Roth, ''twas the drink doing the talking. Count it not against Maeve and Ailill.'

'Nonetheless, Mac Roth, I'll not give up the Brown Bull, at this time.'

So Mac Roth returned to the court of Connacht and told Maeve how the matter had fallen out.

'No need to smooth the knots and polish the knobs,' said she. 'It was well known that if the Brown Bull of Cooley came not freely, it would come by force. And taken it shall be!'

The Rising of the Men of Connacht

A call went out to the men of Connacht and to the provinces of Ireland. Ailill's brothers, six sons of Magach, sent their followers to the number of three thousand. And three thousand more came with the exiles from Ulster, Cormac, son of Conchobor, and Fergus Mac Roig. To Cruachan Ai they all gathered.

The first band of these men had shorn heads, green cloaks about them with silver brooches, and next their skin they wore shirts of gold thread. They carried broad swords with handles of silver.

There was a second, and then a third band. These last men had long hair, yellow-golden and streaming. They wore purple cloaks with gold embroidery, and their long silken shirts reached to their heels. Each man had a shield and a long stabbing spear. Altogether, they lifted their feet and set them down in order.

'Now,' said Maeve gladly, 'Cormac is come, for I see him yonder.'

They pitched camp, and that night they lay under the dense smoke of camp-fires, between the four fords of the rivers. For two weeks they stayed there, drinking and feasting, so that their future journey would be the lighter for them. Then Maeve took her chariot to go and speak with her druid. From him, she would discover the signs and the auguries.

'All who part today from friend or family,' said Maeve, 'and do not return will curse me, for this army is mine.'

'Whoever else falls or fails,' said the druid, 'you yourself will return.'

As they departed, the charioteer wheeled his chariot by the right, to get the power of a good omen, and Maeve saw a thing that surprised her. A young woman with a bright face and thin red lips stood by the pole of the chariot. Her teeth were shining like pearls. As white as night-fallen snow was the lustre of her skin, and her voice was as sweet as the strings of the harp.

'What woman are you,' said Maeve, 'and what is your task?'

'Not hard to tell,' she answered. 'I am Fedelm, the poetess of our Connacht, from the magic *shee* of Cruachan. The learning from Scotland I have, which is the Light of Foreknowledge.'

'Well Fedelm, prophetess, how do you see our army?'

'I see red on them, I see crimson.'

'But my messengers return from Emain Macha,' said Maeve, 'where Conchobor suffers his pains. He cannot stir. Therefore we do not fear the Ulstermen. Speak truly, Fedelm, how do you see our army?'

'Still I see red on them, I see crimson.'

'Red is no matter between armies. Wounds will weep when great forces meet. But Fedelm, prophetess, tell me again, how do you see it?'

'Once more,' said she, 'I see red, I see crimson.'

Then Fedelm began to prophesy, and she foretold Cuchulain to the host of the four provinces of Ireland:

> I see a man, strong in battle,
> Wounds in his fair flesh.
> The hero's light is on his brow,
> The wreath of victory about his head.
>
> A radiant face, amazing to women,
> Cuchulain of Murthemne, man of fame.
> Is it he? I cannot tell.
> But his foe is stained with blood.
>
> He moves through the battle.
> Stop him or die!
> He will lay waste your army.
> I am Fedelm, I conceal nothing.

On a Monday at summer's end, the four provinces of Ireland set out, going southeast through many places into the land of Ulster. Maeve was the last into camp, making a circuit of the army, to see who was ready and who was loath. Foremost and most eager among the troops were the men of Galian from Leinster.

'Why do you praise them above others?' said Ailill.

'Good soldiers,' said Maeve. 'While others are clearing the ground, they have already pitched their tents. While others are setting tents, they are cooking. While others eat, they are ready for the music of harpers. When the others have eaten, they are asleep.'

'They are welcome then,' said Ailill, 'for it is with us they march and fight.'

'Not so. They do it for themselves.'

'Let them remain here then.'

'How can that be?' said Maeve. 'They will take our lands while we are away.'

'Then what shall we do?'

'Kill them,' said Maeve.

'Fie, 'tis a woman's trick,' said Ailill. 'Shame on you.'

Then Fergus, the exile from Ulster, said, 'They are friends. Kill them over my dead body.'

'Fergus, that too is possible,' said Maeve. 'We have enough men to kill you all.'

'Not wise,' replied Fergus. 'Seven chiefs of Munster are my allies, and the bold soldiers of Galian are tied to me by oath. But I shall scatter the troops of Galian among the whole army, so that not five of them shall be together in one place.'

This was done and the host moved on, though in the fetching of food and the hunting of deer it was always one of the Galian men that brought down the prey. Fergus led the army, for he knew the country. Seven years had he been king in Ulster, before exile drove him out. But it was not long before old affection called to him, and he began to lead the army astray, wandering north and south. And he sent a secret warning to Ulster, till Maeve saw what he did.

'Friend Fergus, what wandering path is this?' she said. 'We are straying north and south. Ailill and the army fear treachery. Would you betray us, O Fergus Roig? You have gained much wealth among us, here in your exile.'

'No treachery, Maeve, rest easy,' said Fergus. 'This is my land of Ulster. If I turn and twist, it is to avoid Cuchulain, that mighty warrior.'

A sharp anxiety came to Fergus that Cuchulain could be near, and he warned the men of Ireland to be on their guard. It was a slashing lion they were up against, the doom of enemies, the slaughterer of hosts, the flaming torch: that is to say, Cuchulain, son of Sualtam.

That same day, as the army of invaders went eastward over the moors, Cuchulain and his father came to the pillar-stone at Ard Cuillenn. His father's horses cropped the grass to the bare soil, but Cuchulain's horses bit down to the bedrock.

Then Cuchulain made a hoop of an oak sapling, and cut a message in Ogham on it. He forced the hoop over the pillar-stone, as a warning and challenge to the men of Ireland. And when the army came to that place, Fergus saw the hoop and knew its meaning.

'If you of the four provinces of Ireland ignore this hoop,' he said, 'and do not rest here till one of you has made a similar hoop, standing on one foot and using one hand and one eye as he did, the royal hero who made it will slay you before the dawn hour.'

So the host turned aside and camped in a great wood. Heavy snow fell in the night. It lay up to the shoulders of the men and the flanks of the horses, and all Ireland was a level white plain. Tents could not be set and no food was prepared for lack of fires. All huddled together, white men. Who was friend, who was enemy? Certainly, it was a night of hardship.

As for Cuchulain, he was away that night, being after a woman. But he rose early and scrubbed himself, and yoked his chariot, to find that track of the enemy.

'Alas, Laeg,' he said to his charioteer, 'we were wrong last night to be after a woman. We betrayed our trust. The army of the four provinces has slipped by us. Track the enemy, Laeg, and reckon their number.'

Laeg went after the track but could not read it. Then Cuchulain read the signs and numbered the enemy.

'You are confused in your reckoning, little Cu,' said Laeg.

'Not so,' replied Cuchulain. 'Eighteen divisions have gone by. But the last, that of the men of Galian, is dispersed among the rest.' Cuchulain knew this because of his many powers of insight and knowledge, which were beyond the gifts of other men.

'Friend Laeg,' he said, 'put the whip to the horses, for on my life my weapon must taste some blood before this night.'

So they sped to Ath Gabla where, with a single stroke, Cuchulain cut a forked pole with four prongs, which he set firmly in the ford of the river. As he was doing this, Err and Innel, two stripling sons of Nera, surprised him and vied together to be the first to attack him. But Cuchulain took the heads from the bodies of the warriors and their charioteers, and stuck a head on each prong of the pole.

It was not honourable to take bodies or horses or trappings, so Cuchulain sent the horses homewards to the men of Ireland, with the reins loose over the ears, and the headless trunks dripping red into the chariots. When these came in sight, the van of the army stopped and the rear piled forward, and all were thrown into a great fear.

Maeve was travelling as usual in the midst of her nine chariots, so that the filth and splatter thrown up by the army would not reach and darken her golden diadem. When she saw the bloody remains in the chariots, she thought it was the work of many men, and she sent Cormac, the exiled son of Ulster's king, to spy out the land. At the ford of the river he saw only a forked pole with four heads dripping, and the track of a single chariot drawn by two horses. The nobles of Ireland, following after Cormac, stood amazed at the sight.

'Pitch tents,' said Ailill, 'prepare food and drink, make music and then go to rest, for last night was a terrible night indeed. And Fergus, tell me this: who has come so swiftly and suddenly and killed these four at the ford?'

'Not hard to say,' replied Fergus. 'Who would it be but the little lad Cuchulain, the foster-son of Conchobor the king.'

'I've heard speak of him,' said Ailill. 'What age would this boy be, this little Hound of Culann of Ulster?'

'It is not his age that is most troublesome,' said Fergus, 'for this boy did the deeds of a man long before now. There is no wolf more blood-thirsty, no hero more fierce, no man equal to even a fourth part of Cuchulain's warlike deeds. He is a sledgehammer for smiting, a raven for flesh-tearing, a lion for ferocity. None can measure up to his roar, his speed, his fury, his quick and certain triumphs.'

'No need to scare ourselves,' said Maeve. 'He has only one body. He can be wounded or captured. How can a beardless boy hold out against seasoned, resolute warriors?'

'He may do so,' said Fergus. 'Already, this little fellow is the author of mighty deeds.'

The Youthful Deeds of Cuchulain

'He was reared,' said Fergus, 'in the oak house of his parents on the Plain of Murthemne, hearing day by day the stories of the young lads of Emain Macha. For it was there that King Conchobor of Ulster spent his time. One third of the day the king watched the boys at play and hurling, one third at the chessboard, and one third feasting and drinking till he fell asleep. There is no greater lord and warrior in Ireland than Conchobor. I, Fergus, say it, though he himself banished me into exile.

'Cuchulain longed to join those lads in Emain, but his mother said he was too young and would not let him go. So he set out himself, with his hurley-stick and his silver ball and his sharp little spear which he tossed before him till he came to the field of Emain. Thrice fifty youths and the king's son, Follamain, were playing their games. The little lad went into their midst and caught the ball and kept it close from them and carried it away over the goal.

'"Attack that fellow," cried Follamain. "Let him meet his death. Does he not know that no son of Ulster may join our game unless he has our protection?"

'Then they all attacked him with thrice fifty hurley-sticks and thrice fifty balls. He beat down the sticks and warded off the balls, and struck those boys to the ground, chasing some of them even to the chessboard on the mound where Conchobor was playing. As Cuchulain came leaping over the

112

board, the king caught and held him. '"Now, little fellow," said Conchobor, "you are rough indeed with these boys."

'"Good reason for that," replied Cuchulain. "It is a strange way they have to honour a guest from a distant place."

'"Who are you?" said the king.

'"I am Setanta, son of Sualtam and of your own sister Dechtire."

'Then the king welcomed his sister's son, and told him how it was in Emain, and took him under protection. This little boy who overthrew the sons of warriors and champions was but five years old.'

Thus spoke Fergus, and in a while Cormac, son of Conchobor, took up the story.

'In the next year,' he said, 'that little lad did a second deed. Culann the Smith of Ulster was preparing a feast for Conchobor. Only a few were asked, for Culann was not rich. He had only his hammer and his anvil, his tongs and his fists, to work with.

'As Conchobor was leaving Emain Macha, he went by the field to say farewell to the boys. He saw a wonderful sight. Thrice fifty boys guarded the goal at one end of the field, and at the other end stood a little lad alone. And in the hurling and the throwing the little lad put the ball past the thrice fifty youths, but none of them could go past the lad. Then it came to fighting and wrestling, and the lad stripped them all naked though they could not even pluck the brooch from his cloak.

'The king was astonished and asked the lad to go with him to the feast. But he replied, "Not yet indeed. I shall not leave these fellows till we have had our fill of playing. But I shall follow you." The king took no account of these words. He went on to the house of Culann, and when he was within the smith let loose the guard-dog, a ferocious large bloodhound. It was a wild, savage, surly dog, as strong as a hundred. It lay growling beyond the door, with its shaggy head on its paws.

'In a short time the little boy came following, throwing his hurley ball from hand to hand. When he came to the green before the house, the dog began to bay. It was minded to make a feast of the boy and swallow him entire up to the middle of his breast. As the dog came roaring at him, the little lad cast the ball with all his might into the gaping mouth, and the ball carried the dog's guts out through the back way. Then the boy gripped the dog by the hind legs and dashed it against a large stone so that its limbs jumped from their sockets.

'When the household heard the roars and the commotion, they ran out, fearing that the boy was devoured. They saw that he was safe and welcomed him. Culann also greeted him, but not gladly.

'"I fear now," he said, "my livelihood is wasted, for you have taken my guardian from me."

'"Be not angry," said the boy. "I will rear you a new pup from the best breed in Ireland. And till that pup grows to strength, I myself will be your hound, the keeper of your household, your flocks and your herds."

'Then Cathbad the druid said, "Let him be called Cu-Chulain, the Hound of Culann, because of this, and that name will forever be on the lips of the men of Ireland and Scotland."

'Thus it was that Cuchulain gained his name, and he was but six years old.'

After that, there was a silence, and then Fiachu Mac Firaba spoke out.

'There was another deed that Cuchulain did,' said he, 'when Cathbad the druid was teaching the law and cunning of druids to eight eager pupils, as was always his way. "Master," asked one, "what is the omen for this day?" Cathbad replied that the boy who took up arms on that day would be famous on the tongues of all men, but his days would be short-lived and fleeting.

'When Cuchulain heard this, he threw away his play-things and went to Conchobor to ask for weapons. The king gave him spears and a shield and a sword, but Cuchulain shook them and shattered them. And he did the same with fourteen more sets of arms till Conchobor had no more at

Emain and gave the lad his own weapons. Cuchulain shook these arms and they held, and then Cuchulain saluted the king. When Cathbad saw this, again he warned of the omen, that the life of the boy would be short.

'"Though there would be to me but one day and one night in this world," said Cuchulain, "I would be content so long as my fame and my deeds live after me."

'Then Cathbad said, "Come, little lad, mount this chariot, for it holds the same omen for you."

'Cuchulain mounted the chariot, and it broke under him, and a second and a third also up to the number of seventeen, till Ibar, the king's charioteer, yoked the king's own chariot to the king's horses, and that chariot held. Then Ibar drove Cuchulain around all of Emain Macha and the youths on the playing-field stood and saluted their young companion.

'"Now, little lad," said the charioteer, "let the horses go to the pasture."

'"Not yet," said Cuchulain, "I shall go as far as the road goes."

'So they rode onward to Sliab Fuait, to the border of Ulster. Conall Cernach was the man who guarded the border that day, to welcome poets and to ward off enemies. As he stood, Ulster's champion, at the ford of the river, he heard a little fellow in a chariot say, "Go home now, master Conall, and let me keep watch for the province."

"Nay, little boy," said Conall, "you are too young for war."

"Then I shall go south to the banks of Loch Echtrann, to redden my hands today in the blood of an enemy."

'But Conall would not let him go alone. For a while they travelled in company, then suddenly Cuchulain loosed a stone from his sling and smashed the yoke of Conall's chariot, so Conall could not go on.

"Good aim!" cried Cuchulain. "See, O Conall, I shoot straight. Is that the making of a good warrior?"

'With that, he left Conall and went on to the south. He found no enemy, but at the White Cairn, on the summit of

Sliab Moduirn, the charioteer Ibar showed him the whole extent of the renowned province of Ulster, from mountains to plains, from the rivers to the sea. Below them was the fort of the sons of Nechta Scene, rogues who boasted that they had killed as many Ulstermen as the number still alive. Ibar was afraid to challenge these fierce sons, but Cuchulain laughed at him and went boldly to the fort.

'Where bog and river met they turned loose the horses. At the green before the fort Cuchulain took a hoop of wood with the challenge on it and placed it over the pillar-stone.

'"Now Ibar," said Cuchulain, "take the skins and coverings from the chariot that I may sleep on the grass for a while."

'As he slept, Foill the Deceitful, son of Nechta Scene, came and woke the boy. Angry words passed between them till Foill reached for his arms.

'"Go softly, little lad," said Ibar, "neither points nor sharp edges can hurt that man."

'But Cuchulain sent a ball of tempered metal hurling through Foill's shield onto the flat of his forehead so that his brains went out at the back of his head, and the light of the air was visible as if through a hole in a sieve.

'At once, Tuachall the Cunning, the second son, came running, and he was so fast and nimble hardly any weapon could touch him. But Cuchulain took in hand the great poisoned spear of Conchobor and pierced Tuachall through shield and breast and rib and heart, and struck off his head before the body hit the ground.

'That was the signal for the last of them, Fannall the Swallow, to try his luck.

'"Watch out for this one," said Ibar. "He can travel over water like a swallow. No one can cope with him near water."

'But Cuchulain, who had swum like a salmon in the pools of Emain, clasped his arms around Fannall at the ford, bashed off his head, and let the current run away with the body.

'Then Cuchulain went into the fort and pillaged it and burnt the buildings to the level of the walls. He took the three heads of the sons of Nechta and went away to Sliab Fuait.

'"Let the horses exert themselves," Cuchulain said to Ibar, "because of the storm and pursuit that is after us." And the chariot flew over the Plain of Breg faster even than the wind and the birds.

'Towards Sliab Fuait, they saw a herd of wild deer and it seemed a worthy thing to catch some alive for the men of Ulster. So Cuchulain caught and harnessed two great stags. Then they saw a flock of swans and it seemed a wonderful thing to bring those alive also. With small stones Cuchulain knocked some out of the air, but Ibar was afraid to jump from the racing chariot to fetch them. With one look Cuchulain quelled the fierce bucking and tossing of the galloping stags. Their sharp antlers were stilled, and Ibar went safely past them to get the swans.

'So in this manner they rode back to Emain Macha – wild deer about the chariot, a swan-flock above, and three heads in the hand.

'As they came to Emain, a cry went up, "Some terror is here. A warrior with blood-stained heads under pure white birds. Let us meet and please him, or he may do damage to the men of Emain."

'They sent out to please him the women of Emain, thrice fifty women, all naked, to expose their shame to him. But when he saw all those young women flaunt their naked bodies before him, he hid his face. Then they seized him and plunged him in a vat of cold water, to cool his ardour. The first vat they tried burst its staves, the second vat seethed with bubbles of heat, but the third went from hot to cold as the wrath and the ardour abated.

'He rose from the vat, blushing crimson from head to foot. They dressed him in a tunic with a thread of gold and a green mantle held by a silver pin. He came and stood by Conchobor's knee, and the king stroked his fair yellow hair.

'At seven years old, this little lad did those deeds,' said Fiachu Mac Firaba. 'It is no marvel that we have reason to fear him, now that he has reached seventeen.'

Alarms and Deadly Excursions

As the four provinces of Ireland went eastwards, over the mountain of Cruinn, Cuchulain followed them and came upon a broken chariot. It was the chariot of Orlam, son of Ailill and Maeve. The charioteer stood apart, cutting wood from a holly-tree.

'What is your task?' said Cuchulain.

'Cutting a new chariot-pole. Ours broke chasing that wild deer Cuchulain. Here, friend, lend me a hand, either cutting or trimming.'

Cuchulain began to strip a pole, rubbing it so smooth and polished in his fist that not even a fly might keep a footing on it. When he saw this, the charioteer was surprised.

'Friend, who are you?' he said. 'This work seems beneath a man of your looks.'

'I am that wild Cuchulain you spoke of just now.'

'Alas,' cried the charioteer, 'now I am a dead man!'

'Rest easy,' replied Cuchulain, 'I do not kill servants. But where is your master?'

The charioteer pointed to Orlam, who was resting on a hillock. Then Cuchulain took Orlam by the hair and cut off his head.

'Tie this head to your back,' Cuchulain told the charioteer, 'and do not stop till you reach the middle of your camp. I shall be watching you. There is a stone in my sling, ready to break your head.'

When Ailill and Maeve saw the remains of Orlam, it was a misery and a warning to them. 'This is another thing entirely from catching birds,' said the queen.

Then Cuchulain went about death's business, striking the enemy wherever he found them and taking their heads from them. The men of Ireland were afraid of sudden attack, and they looked on all strangers with cold eyes. Even the tuneful harpers of Cainbile, who had come out of friendship to please the army with music, were taken for Ulster spies and chased mercilessly from the camp. Scattered to the north, amid the stones of Lia Mor, these harpers in their fright turned themselves into deer, for they were both men of music and men of magic.

And Cuchulain went on with his slaughter, one man after another. He had a look on him for Maeve. He swore that if he saw her a stone from his sling would not go far from the side of her head. The first shot he tried killed the pet bird on her shoulder, and the second shot killed a little squirrel on the other shoulder. All the while the list of the slain grew longer.

'I'll make two halves of any man who scoffs at this Cuchulain,' said Ailill. 'Let us hurry to Cooley. If we don't reach there soon, this young fellow will have destroyed two thirds of our host.'

The four provinces of Ireland went on quickly across the plains of Breg and Murthemne, with the warning of Fergus in their ears.

'In truth,' he said, 'though you do not find Cuchulain, he will come to you.'

At the same time, the Brown Bull of Cooley was in the country of Mairgin, pawing the earth and casting up turf and earthworks with his heels. Morrigan, daughter of Ernmas, came from the magic *shee* in the form of a bird. She settled on a pillar-stone and spoke to the bull.

'Be on your guard, you Brown Bull of Cooley, you pitiful one,' she said. 'The men of Ireland aim to carry you off, just like any old ox in a raid.'

So the Brown Bull went, with his fifty heifers, to Sliab Culinn in the north, though the strongest man would be hard put to catch him. These were the virtues of the Brown Bull. He serviced fifty heifers a day, and those that did not calve by the next day burst from the hardness of the begetting. He was so large that fifty youths played hand-ball against his backside, and a hundred warriors took shelter in his shadow from heat and cold. In his bold presence all ghosts and spirits hurriedly departed. In the evening, when he came to his byre, he made a musical lowing that had enough melody and delight in it for any man. That was the power of the Brown Bull of Cooley.

Cuchulain was still shadowing the army, killing the unlucky ones, with his eye open for Maeve. But she remained in the very midst of her host, covered by a canopy of shields, lest Cuchulain should spy her from the hills and strike her with a sling-shot. Daily, she called for bold men to go and do combat with Cuchulain.

'Not I,' said one.

'Certainly not,' said another.

'Nothing is due from me,' said a third. 'Besides, who is strong enough to oppose him?'

Then Maeve sent for Fiachu, one of the exiled Ulstermen, to parley with Cuchulain.

'Trust my welcome,' said Cuchulain, 'and tell me your terms.'

'We offer compensation for damage done to Ulstermen,' replied Fiachu. 'Then entertainment for yourself in Cruachan, with the best wine and mead. And for you also, service with Ailill and Maeve, who will be better for you than that petty lord you now serve.'

'All that is nothing for me,' said Cuchulain. 'I would not change my mother's brother for another king.'

'Well, Maeve and Fergus would speak with you further.'

On the morrow, when Maeve and Fergus went to meet Cuchulain, he seemed to Maeve to be nothing but a boy.

'Speak to him, Fergus,' said Maeve.

'It's yourself should speak,' replied Fergus. 'You're close enough to him, in the narrowness of this glen.'

Then Cuchulain himself spoke up and said to Maeve, 'In virtue of my power, and in the name of those I have slain, I will accept no less than every woman and every milch cow of the men of Ireland.'

But there was no agreement and they parted from each other in anger.

The host of the four provinces camped on the Bird's Ridge for three days and nights, but they had neither food nor music nor rest. Every night, before the bright hour of dawn, Cuchulain killed a hundred warriors.

'This cannot last,' said Maeve. 'We are being destroyed

entirely. Let us offer him the milch cows, and the base-born captive women, so that he may stop his night-work and at least let us sleep. Let Mac Roth, the messenger, take these terms.'

Heavy snow had fallen and the land was white. Cuchulain had cast off the twenty-seven waxed shirts that were bound to his skin with cords, to keep him safe in the fit of his fury. For thirty feet around the snow melted, from the ardour and heat of his body. Such was his condition when Mac Roth approached.

'A single warrior is coming, little Cu,' said Laeg the charioteer.

'What warrior is that?'

'A dark-haired, broad-faced fellow, with a fine cloak about him. A stout tunic next the skin, and two shoes between his feet and the ground. A staff of white hazel in one hand, and a single-edged sword in the other.'

'Those are tokens of a messenger,' said Cuchulain. 'Let us hear him.'

Then Mac Roth came near shouting, 'Where is this famous Cuchulain?'

'What would you say to him,' replied Cuchulain, 'that you would not say to me?' And then Mac Roth offered his terms.

'He whom you seek would not accept those proposals,' said Cuchulain. 'When we feast a guest, let us say a poet or a satirist, the men of Ulster need their cows. As for base-born women, why, our men take them to bed and make more children. Your terms are useless.'

Mac Roth returned to Maeve and said, 'I found a surly, fearsome, fierce fellow between Fochain and the sea. I do not know if he is the famous Cuchulain.'

'Did he accept the terms?' asked the queen.

'Indeed he did not,' replied Mac Roth. And he told them what the man had said.

'Certainly, that was Cuchulain,' said Fergus.

Again, Mac Roth was sent, to ask if Cuchulain would accept any terms.

'If there is one person among you,' replied Cuchulain, 'who knows what I have in mind, I will accept what he says.'

When the message was given to Maeve she looked at the wise and cunning Fergus and he answered at once, 'What he has in mind bodes you no good. He demands that one of us should fight him in single combat every day. When that man has been killed, our army may march on till the next fight is due. If no man comes, then the army shall go no further. And also, while these fights last, Cuchulain is to be fed and clothed by you.'

'Go to him, Fergus,' said Maeve. 'Tell him his terms are good, for it is better to lose one warrior every day than a hundred each night.'

As Fergus was setting out, a young man called Etarcumul wished to go with him, to discover the size and the look of this famous Cuchulain. But Fergus warned him, 'With your pride and arrogance, and his strength and savagery, no good will come of your meeting.'

Still, Etarcumul insisted on going. Fergus and Cuchulain made their agreement, with civil and friendly words, and then Fergus went on his way. But Etarcumul stayed to stare at the Ulster hero.

'What do you gape at?' said Cuchulain.

'You,' he replied.

'Make your eye red with staring, but know that the little creature you are looking at, namely, me, is angry. How do you find me?'

'O fine enough maybe, splendid and handsome. But as for reckoning you among the heroes – the great heroes – we don't count you at all.'

'That is enough speech,' said Cuchulain. 'You came under the protection of Fergus, otherwise only your shattered bones would return to the men of Ireland.'

In great wrath, they agreed to fight in the morning. But Etarcumul could not wait and swung his chariot round a hill and back towards Cuchulain.

'That fighter we just saw, little Cu,' said Laeg, 'he's coming back, and his left chariot-board is turned towards us.'

'A pity to disappoint him,' said Cuchulain. 'Hurry to the ford, Laeg, for I'm the man to give him a fight.'

Then they met at the water's edge, and Cuchulain, out of respect for Fergus, merely cut the sod from under Etarcumul's feet, so that he went tumbling.

'Begone now,' said Cuchulain. 'But for Fergus, I'd have chopped you in pieces, but I won't be washing my hands in your blood today.'

Again, the young man would not leave, and then Cuchulain had patience with him no more. He split him apart from his head to his navel and cut him cross-wise in two. After Etarcumul was dead, Fergus saw the rash fellow's chariot running free, empty of its master, so Fergus wheeled about and reviled Cuchulain.

'Devil,' he cried, 'little demon, what of the pledge you gave me? Do you think my club is too short to strike you?'

'Friend Fergus,' replied Cuchulain, 'do not be angry. Was it better that I should punish that vain fool, or that he should conquer me? The fault was his, as his charioteer will tell you.'

Then Fergus was content. The ankles of Etarcumul were tied to his chariot and he was dragged to the camp. His lungs and his liver knocked on every rough stone till his body was dumped at the tent of Ailill and Maeve.

'What brutality is this?' cried Maeve. 'Where is the guarantee that this monster gave to Fergus? This is how a coward honours his word!'

'Woman, are you mad?' Fergus answered her. 'If it is wise, a common cur does not snap at a bloodhound. Why, even I myself would hardly dare to raise a hand against Cuchulain.'

Then there was nothing else to do but to bury the poor fool Etarcumul.

The Finding of the Bull

Each day, Cuchulain fought in single combat, and in a very short time there was no competition among the four provinces of Ireland to meet him. Anxious to find the bull and stop the slaughter, Maeve went away with a third of her force. But Cuchulain followed closely to guard his territory, for his own land was dearer to him than any other.

Then from the direction of Sliab Culinn came twenty-four cloaked figures, driving the Brown Bull with fifty of his heifers. Buide, son of Ban, was the man in charge. Cuchulain saw the cattle and approached the party.

'From where are these animals?' he asked.

'From off that mountain.'

'And who are you to take them?'

'Buide, son of Ban,' he replied, 'one that neither loves you nor fears you.'

'For you, Buide,' said Cuchulain, 'I have the special gift of a little spear.'

And Cuchulain threw a spear which shattered Buide's ribs and ran into his heart.

While they argued and fought, with shouting and banging of shields the Brown Bull was driven towards the encampment where the men of Ireland were expected that night. The herdsman, who had been captured with the bull, did his best to prevent this. At a narrow gap, he stood in the path of the herd, to turn the cattle aside. But the tumult drove the cattle on, and they trampled the herdsman thirty feet into the ground and made a mincemeat of his body. Now nothing prevented the Brown Bull from falling into the hands of his enemies.

A part of the cattle raid on Cooley was complete, but Maeve had no satisfaction to see that Cuchulain was still close upon her.

'The best man to deal with him,' said the men of Ireland, 'is Cur Mac Dalath, a man unpleasant to be with, a danger to friend and foe. It would be no loss to us if he fell, though better indeed if he were to kill Cuchulain.'

Now Mac Dalath held the little boy of Ulster in contempt, but he went out to meet him with a cartload of weapons. He found Cuchulain practising his warlike moves and his passes at arms. He was practising the Apple feat, and the Edge feat, and the Level Shield feat, and the Little Dart feat, and the Rope feat, and the Feat of Cat, and the Hero's Salmon Leap, and the Pole-cast, and the Breaking of the Sword, and the Champion's Cry. He was doing his running and jumping and dodging and sideway leaping, with many cat-like twists and turns, roaring the while with many fierce shouts and howls. It was hard work indeed to get near him.

For a third of the day Mac Dalath stayed behind the boss of his shield, trying to get a blow in. Cuchulain took no notice. At last, Laeg the charioteer said, 'Little Cu, have the goodness to take a look at this fellow trying to kill you.'

Then Cuchulain suddenly looked up and flung an apple over the shield-rim and knocked a piece of brain the size of a ball out the back of Mac Dalath's head. That was the end of Cur Mac Dalath. After this, many of the men of Ireland cowered in their tents, while a few were sent out unhappily to do combat against Cuchulain. Loth and Srub Daire and Morc and Mac Teora and several others suffered and died. It is tedious to relate so many unlucky names.

There was no help for it but that Maeve must bribe with certain gifts those who had so little desire to meet Cuchulain in battle.

'Who is it,' said Cuchulain to Laeg, 'that will come next to meet me? Go to their camp with greetings to my foster-brother Lugaid. He shall know.'

'It is Ferbaeth,' Lugaid said to Laeg, 'Cuchulain's own kins-man, and mine too. Ferbaeth has gone to the tent of Finnabair, the royal daughter of Maeve and Ailill. It is she who pours the wine for him, and kisses him at every drink. Not for everyone is that liquor, for there's fifty loads of it and no more.'

Now, Cuchulain much disliked it to fight his own foster-brother, a man trained in his own school of weapons. But he made short work of it and removed Ferbaeth forever from the arms of Finnabair.

Next into the tent of Finnabair, to drink and kiss and burst the flock mattress with joy, was Larine. He was brother to Lugaid, a silly proud lad, but a strong-armed fighter. Even in the arms of Finnabair, Larine longed for day, to prove his mettle against Cuchulain. Out he went at first light, with arms of every kind. But the four provinces of Ireland yawned in their tents and turned over, and the women scoffed at his folly.

Cuchulain met him unarmed and took away his weapons, like taking toys from a child. Then he grabbed hold of Larine and crushed him, and squeezed all the excrement out of him till a poisonous gas arose around them. From that time, Larine never woke without complaint and never ate without pain. He had trouble in the gut, and a tightness in the chest, and cramps, and a running at the bowel. But he was the only man to survive single combat with Cuchulain, though he died later from his hurts and weakness.

About this time, Morrigan came to Cuchulain, in the guise of a pretty girl, dressed in many colours.

'I am the daughter of Buan, the Eternal King,' she said. 'Out of love for your fame I have brought you my treasure and my cattle.'

'No good,' replied Cuchulain. 'We are far gone here, famished rather than full. What use is a woman in such a struggle?'

'Women give a kind of help.'

'Do you think I make war for a woman's soft thighs?'

Then Morrigan turned on him and said, 'If not my help, then take my hindrance. When you fight, in the shape of an eel I'll entangle your feet. In the shape of a grey wolf I'll drive the cattle over you. In the shape of a red heifer I'll lead the herd that tramples you into the mud.'

Soon, when Loch, son of Mofemis, came to do battle at the ford, Cuchulain found a slippery eel tripping his feet, and a grey wolf howling the cattle into fright, and a red heifer leading the thunder of the stampede. Cuchulain squashed the eel in the fork of his toes, and took an eye out of the wolf with his sling-shot, and smashed the legs of the heifer from under it. But all the time Loch was hacking at him and drawing the life-blood from his body. In high anger, when he was free to turn on Loch, Cuchulain pierced the heart in his breast with a barbed spear and his spirit fled away.

'Give me a favour,' cried the dying man. 'Step back a pace, so I may fall to the east and not the west.'

'A warrior's request,' said Cuchulain, 'and I shall grant it.'

So Loch died for all men to see that his face was still toward the enemy.

Then Cuchulain was weary and wounded, and he called aloud in his sore distress:

Go forth, friend Laeg, and rouse the men of Emain.
Tell them I am sore wounded, blood drips from my
    weapon.
Tell Conchobor I stand alone at many fords.
I cannot hold the enemy, with only Laeg for friend.

Loch has mangled my hips, the she-wolf has bitten
    me,
The eel tripped me and Loch punished my liver.
Ulstermen, give battle to Maeve and Ailill,
While I'm here in sorrow, blood-flecked and
    wounded.

While he was calling in this despair, hag Morrigan came again from the magic hill of the *shee* in the shape of a one-eyed crone, milking a cow with three teats. She knew that only Cuchulain himself could cure her from the wounds he had given her. In his weakness and thirst, Cuchulain begged for a drink, and she gave him the milk of one teat. But his thirst still raged and she gave him the milk of the other two teats.

'A blessing on you, woman,' said he. 'May she who gives be quickly healed.'

And at once she was cured of the three blows Cuchulain had given her, when she was in the form of an eel and a wolf and a heifer.

The Great Sixfold Slaughter

The four provinces of Ireland pitched their camp in the Plain of Murthemne. Cuchulain kept watch on them, close by

127

the fire that Laeg kindled against the night cold. Far off, Cuchulain saw the fiery glitter of the bright gold weapons in the setting sun. Rage filled him once more at the multitude of his enemy. He shook his arms and uttered a hero's roar. All the demons of the air gave answer, and Nemain, the war-goddess, brought confusion on the men of Ireland. They clashed their weapons to raise their courage, but a hundred fell before the night was done. The agreement was broken. No more was there single combat only. Carnage and blood-lust held the field.

In the morning, Laeg saw a solitary man coming from the enemy camp.

'What man is that?' asked Cuchulain.

'Soon told,' said Laeg. 'A tall, broad, fair man, close-cropped. A royal cloak about him, and a hard black shield in his hand. Wonderful is his work with spear and forked javelin. But no one is heeding him. Is it that they cannot see him?'

'True for you, friend Laeg,' said Cuchulain. 'It is a good spirit from the *shee* come to help me in my sore distress, as I stand alone against the four provinces of Ireland.'

'I am Lug, son of Ethlenn,' said the strange warrior, 'your spirit-father from the magic world of the *shee*. Sleep, little Cu, for your wounds are heavy upon you. I will hold the line against the men of Ireland.'

For three days and nights Cuchulain slept at Ferta, and the depth of his sleep matched the extent of his weariness. From the Monday of summer's end to the Wednesday of the beginning of spring he had not slept but only dozed a little, leaning on his spear, with his head resting on his fist. All the rest of the time he was striking and cutting and slaying and hacking the warriors of the four great provinces of Ireland.

Then Lug took plants from the *shee*, and healing herbs and curing charms, and he cleaned and bathed all the wounds and gashes of Cuchulain's body. Thus, in his sleep, Cuchulain was quietly healed.

At the end of three days Cuchulain awoke. He was revived

and ruddy with health. He was ready for a march or a feast or a battle or love-making. But he cried out, 'Alas, that I was not in my full mind and strength, for the youths that fell in the days of my sleep would not have done so.'

'Good words, little Cu,' said Lug. 'But be content. There is no stain on your honour, and your courage is no less.'

'Then stay, O warrior from the *shee*, and we will avenge the dead youths together.'

'Indeed I will not stay,' replied Lug. 'No man can match your bravery, or outdo your fame. Go on alone. At this time, none has power over your life.'

Then Cuchulain said to Laeg, 'Yoke the scythed chariot.'

Laeg got ready the chariot and then dressed himself in the manner of a hero. Carefully he looked at every point of his arms and armour, and he did not forget to cast a protective spell on both his horses and his companions. Today he prayed for the three gifts of the driver of horses – the leaping of the gap, the unerring driving, and the handling of the whip.

When the chariot was ready, Cuchulain put on his battle-array. First came the twenty-seven stiff, waxed shirts bound to his skin with cord. Over these he strapped on a jerkin of hard leather, made from seven yearling ox-hides. From this jerkin, spears or arrows fell back as if from stone. Then he put on a coat of smooth, fine silk bordered with gold, and he covered that with a surcoat of soft, black pliable leather. When he was dressed, he took up his arms: his ivory-hilted sword, his five-pronged spear, his javelin, his darts, his sling-shot, his curved shield with a rim so sharp it could shave hairs.

Lastly, he put on his great crested war-helmet, from which his howling battle-cry echoed and re-echoed like the roars and shouts of a hundred warriors. And from the helmet there came also the screams of devils and demons ringing in the air all about him, foretelling the bloodshed of many warriors. He wrapped about him his cloak of concealment, brought as a gift from the Land of Promise by the sea-god Manannan Mac Lir. Then he was ready.

The rage-fit was upon him. He shook like a bulrush in the stream. His sinews stretched and bunched, and every huge, immeasurable, vast ball of them was as big as the head of a month-old child. His face as a red bowl, fearsomely distorted, one eye sucked in so far that the beak of a wild crane could scarcely reach it, and the other eye bulged out of his cheek. Teeth and jawbone strained through peeled-back lips. Lungs and liver pulsed in his throat. Flecks of fire streamed from his mouth. The booming of his heart was like the deep baying of bloodhounds, or the growl of lions attacking bears.

In virulent clouds, sparks blazed, lit by the torches of the war-goddess Badb. The sky was slashed as a mark of his fury. His hair stood about his head like the twisted branches of red hawthorn. A stream of dark blood, as tall as the mast of a ship, rose out of the top of his head, then dispersed into dark mist, like the smoke of winter fires.

Then the hero sprang into his scythed chariot, with its bright blades and points of iron. The horses were lithe, fast-leaping, high-prancing, great-hooved. Cuchulain drove at his enemy, the warriors of the four provinces of Ireland, and performed his thunder-feat. He killed a hundred, two hundred, even five hundred. He did not think it too much, for he was now in full battle with the army of invaders. He remembered the wrongs done to Ulster.

He attacked with hatred in his heart, circling the enemy, throwing up great ramparts of corpses. Round and round he went, three times, leaving six layers of bodies lying foot to foot and neck to headless neck. Who can tell the full number of the slain? But not one in three of the men of Ireland escaped without the loss of an eye, or a broken thighbone, or a trench in the side of the head. Six score and ten kings did Cuchulain slaughter on the Plain of Murthemne, and a countless number of hounds, horses, women and children besides.

This was the Sixfold Slaughter of the Cattle Raid of Cooley. It was one of the three greatest slaughters ever seen.

The Encounter with Ferdiad

How could the four provinces of Ireland stand against Cuchulain? Now only Ferdiad, son of Daman, seemed man enough to protect them, a warrior with a skin of horn, and Cuchulain's own foster-brother.

But Ferdiad refused. He would not fight the friend of his youth, his foster-brother, his little Cu. Maeve sent druids and satirists to lampoon him and spite him and raise on his face the three blisters of shame, blemish and disgrace. Then for the sake of his honour Ferdiad went with Maeve's messengers, for he thought it better to die by the stroke of the sword than by the shafts of satire and reproach. In the camp of the men of Ireland, Ferdiad was greeted with respect. Strong liquor was pressed on him till he was merry and drunk. Fair Finnabair sat next to him, knee to knee, and gave him three kisses with every drink, and sweet apples plucked from the bosom of her dress.

Then Maeve spoke softly to him and said, 'Listen, O Ferdiad, to the rewards I offer you: a chariot worth four times seven bondmaids, clothes for a dozen men, a piece of the Plain of Ai, and freedom from tribute for you and yours for ever. This brooch I wear you shall also have, and my daughter Finnabair as your wedded wife. Is that not enough? Then take your pleasure as well from my own firm thighs.'

''Tis much,' said Ferdiad, 'but still I would rather not fight.'

'Then it is true,' replied Maeve with her usual cunning, 'what Cuchulain says, that it would be no great feat of arms for him to kill you.'

'He should not have said that,' Ferdiad answered. At once he gave his promise and prepared for the fight.

Now, when this became known to Fergus, he feared for his foster-son Cuchulain, for Ferdiad was a mighty warrior, and kinsmen had no business fighting each other. Fergus yoked his chariot and went to warn Cuchulain.

'Your own foster-brother Ferdiad, son of Daman, is coming against you,' he told Cuchulain.

'Bad news,' said Cuchulain. 'Out of love and affection I wish to avoid him. But if he comes armed to the ford, I swear the point of my sword will make his body sway and fall like reeds in the spring flood.'

That night, Ferdiad slept heavily but woke with the dawn, no longer drunk and merry, but starting up in full anxiety. He ordered the horses to be harnessed, but when the chariot was ready, he turned aside.

'Heavy I am with care and anxiety,' he said to the charioteer. 'Spread the skins and the coverings and I shall sleep some more.'

But Cuchulain was up by now. He mounted and advanced to the ford amid noise and uproar, the ringing of breastplates, the creek of harness and chariots, the drumming of hooves.

'Up, up, sir,' cried Ferdiad's charioteer. 'A large man comes, rising high out of his chariot. It is Cu the Hound, bright and deadly as steel.'

'Enough, man, praise him no more,' said Ferdiad. 'Make ready my weapons. I'll meet him at the ford.'

So they advanced, one from each side of the stream.

'In the matter of greetings,' Cuchulain called out, 'it is more fitting that I welcome you. For it is you that have invaded my country and province.'

'Little Cu,' Ferdiad replied, 'why do you mean to fight me? When we were youths, you were the helper who tended my spear and prepared my bed.'

'True indeed. But then I was young and small. That is not the way I am today.'

With many bitter reproaches they broke their friendship, and they threw at each other insults and strong words and taunts and threats.

'The malice and meddling of Ailill and Maeve have sent you here,' said Cuchulain, 'but things go badly for all who face me. And all for the sake of Finnabair! You will never wed her. She has deceived many men and will destroy you too.'

'Enough speech,' said Ferdiad. 'Now let us fight. Remember, little Cu, the feats of arms we practised with the masters of our youth? Let us put them to use.'

First, they threw darts and javelins so thick and fast that

they hummed in the air like the bees of summer. Then from midday to nightfall they hurled smooth-polished spears, evading the shields, making each other a red mess of gore and blood. 'Let us cease now,' they cried to the setting sun, and they handed their weapons to the charioteers.

Then they threw out their arms and kissed each other, and they went to rest on beds of fresh rushes and soft pillows. Their horses grazed together and their charioteers settled around the same fire. Of the herbs and charms brought for Cuchulain's wounds, he sent a portion across the stream for the healing of Ferdiad. And of the food and strong drink brought for Ferdiad's hunger, he sent a portion across the stream to raise the strength in Cuchulain.

So they went out on the second day. They fought again from dawn to night, till they went to their beds all bloodied and sore. But next morning, as they approached, Cuchulain said, 'Your look is not good today. Your hair is dark and dull, your eyes overcast, your figure drooping.'

''Tis not from fear of you,' said Ferdiad. 'There's no man in Ireland who can defeat me.'

But Cuchulain pitied him. 'Ferdiad, is it truly you?' he said. 'Sure it is that you are utterly doomed. Why do you fight your foster-brother for the sake of that woman?'

'O Cuchulain, noble warrior,' Ferdiad replied, 'all men must make the journey to the cold sod of the grave. Our darts and spears have settled nothing. Let us resolve the matter with our hard-smiting swords.'

They hacked and hewed and cut lumps from each other as big as fists, but no result came of this sword-play. Next day, Ferdiad came early to the ford. He felt the time of victory or defeat was on him, and he began to practise the brilliance of his war-feats.

'Laeg, look yonder,' said Cuchulain in admiration, 'those are the bold tricks and passes aimed at me.'

'Beware,' said Laeg, 'lest he will chastise you as a mother corrects her child. He will hammer you as flax is beaten in a pond. He will grind you as a mill grinds malt. He will pierce you as an axe splits oak.'

This day, they came together like charging bulls. Once more, the rage-fit was on Cuchulain. He grew huge, like an inflated bladder, and towered high over Ferdiad. In the closeness of the encounter, their heads and hands and feet knocked together and meddled with each other. The fury of their footwork thrashed the water out of the river-bed. Ferdiad caught Cuchulain below his guard and brought a torrent of blood from his wounded breast.

Then Cuchulain called for his barbed spear, which pierced and could not be withdrawn unless the flesh was cut away. Ferdiad saw it and took shelter, crouched low behind his shield. But too late. The spear drove through his thick apron of iron and entered Ferdiad at his backside, and filled every cranny of him with its barbs.

'Now I fall,' cried Ferdiad. 'My ribs are broken, my heart is gore. O why did I fight? Cu, little Hound, I am finished.'

When Cuchulain saw the end of Ferdiad, he ran forward and lifted him bodily.

'Madness and grief constrict me,' he lamented, 'after this deed. Alas, Ferdiad, I am sad that you did not follow the advice of Fergus. Sad indeed that you were deceived by the promises of the false woman of Connacht, fair-haired Maeve. No hero's hand hacked warrior's flesh so well as yours, O Ferdiad, companion of my youth.'

'Tug the guts over the stream,' said Laeg to Cuchulain, 'so the spoils will belong to us.'

But Cuchulain only looked at the body for a long time. Then he said, 'Strip him, friend Laeg, that I may see the brooch of Maeve for which noble Ferdiad did this battle.'

The clothes were stripped and the brooch removed, and then Cuchulain spoke again. 'Cut open the body, friend Laeg, and take out my barbed spear, for I cannot fight without that weapon.'

Laeg did so, and the blood and offal poured on the ground. Again, Cuchulain cried out, 'My weapon is crimson, your blood is drained, O Ferdiad, companion of my youth. Sad what befalls us, my foster-brother, one battle for both of us. But at the end of it there stands your death and my life.'

'Well, little Cu,' said Laeg, 'leave this ford now. We have been here too long.'

'Truly, it is time to leave,' said Cuchulain. 'But every battle I ever had now seems but play and sport after this fight with Ferdiad.'

The Men of Ulster Awake from their Pains

While these things were happening, Sualtam, the father of Cuchulain, heard of the distress of his son, fighting against so many.

'Is it the sky that cracks,' cried Sualtam, 'or the sea bursting, or the splitting of the earth? Or is it the howl of my son, alone in the face of the multitude?'

Hurriedly he came to help his son, but Cuchulain was wary of his help, for his father was only a middling fighter.

'Go rather to Emain Macha and to the men of Ulster,' Cuchulain said to him, 'and rouse them from the sloth of their pains. I can no longer protect them. I have been fighting from summer's end to the beginning of spring, and there is no point of my body, from hair to foot, where a needle might touch without blood on its tip.'

So Sualtam went and cried out to the men of Emain, 'Listen, O Ulstermen, men are being murdered, women raped, cattle plundered!'

Again and again he shouted this message. But he raised no answer, for none could speak before the king, and Conchobor never spoke before his druids. At long last, Cathbad the druid spoke out.

'Who is this,' he asked, 'that murders, rapes, and plunders?'

'It is Ailill and Maeve of Connacht,' replied Sualtam, 'who ravage your land, kill your folk, steal your cattle. Cuchulain alone holds in check the four provinces of Ireland. He is ragged and sore and his joints are bursting. A hazel twig secures his cloak, wisps of straw staunch his wounds.'

Then said Conchobor the king, 'A little too loud is your cry, O Sualtam. The sky still holds, the earth is firm, the sea is calm. As for those warriors from the four provinces of

Ireland, I shall bring back from them every woman of Ulster to her home, and every cow to its byre. Let Finnchad of the Horned Helmet muster our army. Now the men of Ulster are awake from their pains.'

It was an easy task for Finnchad. All the princes and chieftains of Ulster had been waiting for Conchobor to recover and speak.

'We will not wait for the laggards,' said the king. 'We will catch the men of Ireland before they know that I have risen from my pains.'

Large hosts gathered on each side. Three thousand chariots were with Conchobor and Celtchar. The Connachtmen were ranged against them. Then Celtchar called out to his king, 'A hundred druids lead us, good men are at your back, O Conchobor. Let the warriors prepare for battle at Garech and Ilgarech!'

That same night, in the tents of the four provinces of Ireland, Dubthach of the Black Tongue cried out in his sleep:

> Fearful morning, monstrous time,
> Armies ravaged, kings undone
> Necks broken, blood on the sun.
> Host of Ulster – Conchobor's men –
> From that quarter red death comes.

Warriors burst into wakefulness, startled by prophecies and doomsaying. Nemain, goddess of war, muddled their wits. They clanged their weapons and struck about them wildly so that a hundred were killed.

'We have taken their women and their cattle,' Ailill shouted, 'we have levelled their hills. Why wait for their army any longer? Let us spy out a battle-ground on the broad plain of Meath.'

Mac Roth, the messenger, went forward, but soon he heard a thunder of tumult. The earth seemed to be in motion. Wild beasts poured over the plain like winter floods. But wise Fergus knew the cause of this. 'The din and uproar,' he said, 'is the work of Ulstermen attacking the woods. Champions and warriors are clearing the trees from the path of their chariots. It is this that has driven the animals over the land.'

Again Mac Roth went to spy the country. He saw a grey mist between sky and earth, and in the gaps there seemed to be caverns or islands in a lake. A pure white curtain like sifted snow hung before his eyes. In it he saw points of light that might have been shimmering birds, or the stars of a frosty night, or the sparks of a great fire. A strong wind tried to tear the hair from his head.

When all this was told to Fergus, again he knew the cause.

'Not hard to tell,' he said. 'It is the Ulster heroes on the march. The grey mist is the heavy breath of horses and men. The heads of the warriors, standing tall in the chariots, are the islands, and the caverns are the gaping mouths of angry horses from which drop the froth and spittle that makes the pure white curtain. The points of light are the fierce eyes of the warriors sparkling from the beauty of their rich helmets.'

'All this is of no account,' said Maeve, 'we have good soldiers to oppose them.'

'It may not be so,' Fergus warned. 'You will not find in Ireland or Scotland any warriors to match the Ulstermen when the rage-fit is upon them.'

The two armies advanced in sight of each other and halted in Slemain Mide. Then Maeve spoke to her chief counsellors.

'Let us make a good swift plan,' said she. 'Yonder huge, vehement fellow who would attack us is Conchobor, king of Ulster and son of the High-king of Ireland. Draw up our host in open array, face to face with the enemy. Take prisoners rather than kill, for those who oppose us are just the number of prisoners we need.'

While she was speaking, the Ulstermen began to muster on the hill, and they kept coming from dawn to twilight. By the hour of night they were all settled, each chieftain with the full number of his war-band ranged around the king.

'Well now, Mac Roth,' said Ailill, 'relate for us the number and the look of the enemy.'

Cuscraid the Stammerer was there, Conchobor's son, with the silver bands of victory on his spear. Next to him was handsome Sencha, he of the eloquent tongue. Tall Eogan, from the north, brandished his long sword, which was ornamented with ivory from walrus tusks. Near him was grizzled Loegaire, yellow-eyed, gaunt, merciless in close combat. At the head of a large troop was a scarred red face beneath a bush of black hair. It was thick-necked Muremur, son of Gerrcend. Connud Mac Morna curled his pretty hair. A salmon-brooch of bright metal held his long cloak. But he was a lion in heart and hard in battle.

Spreading over the hill, at the head of strong battalions, were many other bold and mighty men – stiff-necked champions, flaming torches of war, heroes, ridge-poles of the army, dragons, thunderbolts, destroyers, boars and breech-makers, the god-blessed and the battle-mad. Tight-knit, they closed their ranks around Conchobor the king.

'But who is he?' said Ailill to Fergus. 'I mean that wrathful, big-nosed, large-eared, coarse-haired, thick-lipped, great-bellied, ill-favoured one.'

'He is half of the battle,' replied Fergus, 'the head of the strife. He is the storm-wave that drowns, the sea that floods over. It is mighty Celtchar, from Lethglas in the north.'

Then Mac Roth said, 'I am tired of all this describing, but there is one more thing to say. I heard one last outcry spreading both east and west.'

'Indeed we know it,' replied Fergus. 'It is Cuchulain struggling off his sick-bed, trying to rise for battle despite his wounds and gashes. The men of Ulster hold him back, for he is unfit to fight after his combat with Ferdiad. They have tied him to his sick-bed with hoops and bands and ropes.'

The Final Battle

In the night Morrigan sowed strife and despondency between the camps. In darkness she sang:

The beak of the raven in the neck of men,
Blood will gush, flesh will be hacked.
Madness of battle, the warrior's storm,
Ruin descends on Cruachan's men,
Grief to Ireland, but to Ulster, all hail!

This woe whispered in Connachtmen's ears. In the same night, the voices of Nemain and Badb, sisters of war, summoned the men of the four provinces of Ireland to meet their fate on the fields of Garech and Ilgarech. When they heard this, many died wholly of fright. Surely it was a bad night for them.

Next morning, all the men of Ulster rose together at the call of their king. They rose stark naked but for the weapons in their hands. In their haste they trampled their tents to make a short way towards the enemy. This news reached Cuchulain, as he lay nearby at Fedan Collna.

But King Conchobor said to Sencha, 'Hold the men back. Look to the omens first. Let no man dare move before the rising sun.'

As they watched they saw the sun rise up golden, without blemish, radiating into the valley and filling all the wide glen.

'Now rouse the men of Ulster, bold Sencha,' said the king, 'for the time of battle has arrived.'

Then both armies took their weapons in hand and began to strike and hew and cut and slay and slaughter each other for a long time. This tumult was loud music to Cuchulain on his sick-bed, and he called out, 'How goes the fighting now, friend Laeg?'

'Bravely, most bravely,' replied he. 'My chariot could ride their backs from end to end, so thick are they on the battle-field.'

'Alas,' cried Cuchulain, 'that I have not the strength to be there.'

'Rest easy, little Cu. It is no disgrace for you. Your task is done.'

Then the armies on both sides re-doubled their efforts to strike and hew and cut and slay and slaughter each other for a long time.

In the midst of this battle Maeve saw that the hands of Fergus were idle.

'It is fitting, O Fergus,' she said, 'that you add your strength to our fight. When you were banished from your own country, we gave you help and land and kindness.'

'Had I but my sword today,' replied Fergus, 'I would cut the trunks of men and pile them high, and the limbs of Ulstermen scattered by me would be as numerous as the stones of a hailstorm.'

So Ailill sent a servant quickly for his own sword and gave it to Fergus. When he had it, Fergus struck so fiercely and mercilessly against the men of Ulster that Conchobor himself hurried forward to stem this rout. He raised his shield in front of Fergus, who gave it three strong brutal blows. The shield strained and groaned, and all the shields of Ulster groaned with it. But it held.

'Who holds this shield against me at Garech and Ilgarech?' cried Fergus.

'One younger and mightier than you,' replied Conchobor, 'one nobler also, who banished you from your territory and estate to live with deer and foxes. Make no attempt now to measure the length of your stride in your own land, you who are dependent on the charity of a woman, you who are already guilty of the death of the sons of Usnech. I, Conchobor, king of Ulster, repulse you and drive you back to the four provinces of Ireland.'

Fergus grasped the sword in both hands and swung it back till the point touched the ground. His intent was to strike three terrible blows, to make the Ulster dead outnumber the living. But Cormac, the exiled son of Conchobor, threw two arms about him.

'Angry and ungentle is this, O Fergus,' he cried. 'Remember that the days of your life began in Ulster.'

'Away from me, fellow,' shouted Fergus. 'I'll not live this day unless I give three mighty blows against Ulster.'

'Then turn your aim elsewhere,' said Cormac. 'Cut the tops from the hills above the battle-field, if that will appease your anger.'

Now the sword Fergus held was a sword from the magic mounds of the *shee*. When it struck it grew as big as the rainbow. So Fergus turned his hand level and cut off the tops of the three hills. They fell into the marsh below, leaving above the three Bald Heads of Meath.

On his sick-bed, Cuchulain heard the clang of sword on shield and said to Laeg, 'who dares to strike the shield of Conchobor while I am alive?'

'It is the hero Fergus,' Laeg told him. 'His sword grows as big as the rainbow. Slaughter slips from it like dross.'

Cuchulain struggled with his bonds while two false poetesses mocked his sickness with satire and feigned tears.

'Quick, friend Laeg,' he cried, 'cut me free of hoops and cords.'

In a twinkling this was done and he sprang from his bed. His first effort was to catch the poetesses and clash their heads like eggshells till their skulls oozed red blood and grey brains, even though his own wounds pulled apart and burst out the dressing of straw and moss that staunched them. His chariot was unyoked, his weapons not ready. But his eagerness was such that he took the body of his chariot up on his back and ran towards the battle.

'Ho, you there, Fergus,' he roared, 'turn and face me. I will scour you like washing in a tub. I will stoop like a hawk on a lark. I will abase you as if under a cat's tail. I'll grind your bones.'

'Who in Ireland dares to speak to me like that?' said Fergus.

'I, Cuchulain, your own foster-son. Your lot falls due. Now give way before me.'

Then Fergus turned and ran with mighty strides, and the men of Ireland went with him, routed towards the west. It was midday when Cuchulain joined the battle. At sunset the last band of Connachtmen fled over the hill. Nothing was left of Cuchulain's chariot but a fistful of spokes and a broken shaft.

The Battle of the Bulls

Under the shelter of shields, Maeve covered the retreat of the four provinces of Ireland. Quickly, she sent the Brown Bull of Cooley into Connacht by a safe route, with fifty heifers and eight guards, so that the Bull, if no one else, would arrive at Cruachan as she had sworn.

Then Maeve felt the monthly issue of her blood.

'Cover the retreat of the men of Ireland,' she said to Fergus, 'till I relieve myself.'

'By all the gods,' cried Fergus, 'this is ill-timed!'

'No help for it,' she replied, 'I must do it or die.'

So Fergus guarded the retreat while Maeve relieved herself. Three trenches she filled, each big enough for a household, in the field called the Foul Place of Maeve. Cuchulain, chasing the retreat, found her there. But he held his hand, for he would not strike her from behind.

'Grant me a favour today,' she said when she saw Cuchulain.

'Well?'

'Safeguard this army in retreat, at least till the men of Ireland have one westward past Ath Mor.'

Cuchulain granted this, and the host slowly marched westward while Fergus watched.

'A fitting end,' he said to the queen, 'to a shambles led by a woman.'

But Maeve replied with spirit, 'It was a band of foals led by a mare into unknown country. We perished for lack of good counsel.' And so the broken remnant of the four provinces of Ireland limped back to Cruachan.

As for the Brown Bull of Cooley, when he saw the beautiful strange land of Connacht he bellowed three times. Finnbennach, the White-horned heard him and advanced to the challenge. But who would judge this contest? Bricriu, son of Carbad, was the most just of men, for he favoured his friend no more than his enemy. He was the best man to judge, and he went to the gap where the bulls would fight.

Then the bulls pawed the ground and threw up fountains of earth. Their cheeks swelled like bellows in a forge. They rushed together, goring and thrusting with their horns. In the midst of their chasing and thundering, Bricriu could not avoid their trampling and was crushed to death. Such was the sad death of Bricriu.

The White-horned gored the side of the Brown Bull and stirred his inward guts. When Cormac saw this happen, he took a spear and gave the Brown Bull three jabs from head to tail.

'O wonderful treasure is this brute to us,' said Cormac, 'that cannot defend himself against a calf. Rouse yourself, bull of Cooley, men on both sides have died for you.'

The Brown Bull heard this, for he had human understanding. He roused himself. In his rage he whirled in a circle and smashed the leg of the white-horned. Still they fought on till the sun set, and even throughout the night the men of Ireland could hear bellows and uproar echoing throughout the bounds of the whole land. And in the morning, when they awoke in Connacht, they saw the Brown Bull coming from the west to Cruachan with the mangled mass of Finnbennach hanging from his horns.

Fergus saw them coming and said, 'Well now, men, let them be. White-horned or Brown Bull, great things have been witnessed here.'

And the men of Connacht meddled no more with the Brown Bull of Cooley. The bull went forward, fiercely shaking the remains of the White-horned all over Ireland. The liver of Finnbennach he left at Cruachan. The loin came to rest at Ath Mor. The thigh was thrown as far as Port Large. The rib-cage landed at Ath Cliath, later called Dublin.

At last, in his rampage across the land, the Brown Bull turned north and saw the summit of Sliab Breg, and he knew that he had come to the land of Cooley. Still in his rage, he turned on the women and children who had gathered to wonder at him, and he did great killing among them. But when he saw what he had done, he turned his back on the hill and his heart broke like a nut in his breast.

Ailill and Maeve made peace with Cuchulain and the men of Ulster. The men of Connacht were in their own land, and the men of Ulster returned to Emain Macha with their great triumph. And for seven years there was no more killing among all the provinces of Ireland.

5

UNDER THE
SPELL
OF LOVE

My body is out from my control,
It has fallen to her share.
I am in two pieces,
Now my bright gentle one is gone.

She was one of my feet, one of my sides –
Her face like the white-thorn –
I was hers more than mine,
She was half my eyes, half my hands.

She was the half of my body,
The fresh torch.
I am faint as I tell it –
She was the very half of my soul.

PWYLL
AND
RHIANNON

Once, when Pwyll was in Arberth with a great host of his men, he wished to stretch his body after the feast and he walked towards a low hill.

'Lord,' said one of the court, 'it is the virtue of this hill that whoever sits upon it will not go from it without wounds or blows, or the sight of a wonder.'

'Wounds or blows I do not fear,' said Pwyll, 'and as to the wonder, I would gladly see it.'

So they sat on that mound, and soon there came along the way a lady in shining brocaded silk on a big, fine, pale white horse. The horse ambled at an even pace. But when Pwyll sent a rider after the lady, no matter how much he put his spurs to his horse, he could not catch up with her.

The same happened on the next day, and the next. However fast the pursuer went, he could not reach the lady. The more he spurred on his horse, all the further was she from him. At last, Pwyll himself took his horse and drove it to its utmost speed. But when he saw it was idle to chase after her, he called out, 'Maiden, in the name of love, stay for me.'

'Gladly,' she answered, 'and it had been better for the horse if you had asked this long since.'

The lady waited for him, and then she drew her veil from her face and they began to talk. He looked on her and thought that the face of every woman he had ever seen was unlovely compared with her.

'Lady,' said he, 'tell me your errand.'

'My errand,' she replied, 'it was to see you. I am Rhiannon, the daughter of Hefeydd the Old, and I am promised to a husband against my will. Out of love for you, I will have no other man, unless you reject me. It is to hear your answer that I am come.'

'Between me and God,' said Pwyll, 'if I had choice of all the ladies in the world, 'tis you I would choose.'

So they were pleasing to each other, and they made a tryst to meet in a year, when a great feast for his coming would be ready in her father's court.

'Lord,' then said Rhiannon, 'if I am not to go to another man, keep you your promise.'

In a year they met again and seated themselves for a feast in the court of Hefeydd. As they were eating they saw enter a tall, auburn-haired, regal youth who came boldly before the company.

'A welcome to you, friend,' said Pwyll, 'take a place among us.'

'I will not,' said he. 'I am a suitor, and I come to ask a boon of you.'

'Whatever you ask,' said Pwyll, 'so far as I can get it, it shall be yours.'

'Alas,' cried Rhiannon, 'why do you give such an answer?'

'Lady, he has given it in the presence of nobles,' said the stranger. 'Now, my lord, this is my request. The lady I love best is to sleep with you this night. I have come to ask for her, and for this feast I see before me.'

Then Pwyll was silent till Rhiannon upbraided him. 'Be dumb as long as you will,' said she, 'for never has a man made more feeble use of his wits. That is the person I was promised to against my will. It is Gwawl, son of Clud, a rich and powerful man. Now you have given your word, bestow me on him lest you dishonour yourself.'

'Lady, what answer is that?' said Pwyll. 'How can I do what you say?'

Then Rhiannon took Pwyll to the end of the hall and said, 'Bestow me upon him, and I shall ensure that he never has me. I shall make a tryst with him for a year from tonight, to sleep with me. And I will offer then a feast for him and his men. Let you be standing by, up yonder in the orchard, in shabby clothes, with a little bag I shall give you, and a hundred horsemen with you. When he is in mirth at the feast, enter with this bag in your hand and ask for nothing but the bag full of food. I will bring it about that not even the produce of seven counties would fill that bag.

'And he shall say, "Will this bag ever be full?"

'"It will not," you shall say, "unless a great man of power shall press it down with both his feet."

'So he shall tread down the food in the bag. Then quickly gather the bag over his head and knot the thong in the mouth. When he is tied, blow a blast on the hunting-horn about your neck, as a signal for your horsemen to fall upon the court.'

While thus they spoke privately, Gwawl grew impatient. 'Give me your answer,' he demanded in anger. So Pwyll granted his request, and he promised a tryst and a feast for Gwawl at the end of a year.

At the appointed time, Gwawl came eagerly to the court of Hefeydd and a welcome was given him. Beyond, in the orchard, Pwyll hid with his hundred men, and he was coarsely dressed with rags on his feet. When he heard laughter within, Pwyll entered with humble looks and asked a boon.

'Ask within reason,' said Gwawl, 'and you shall surely have it.'

'It is only for hunger. The boon I ask is this little bag full of food.'

Then servants arose and began to fill the bag. But for all that went into it, it was no fuller than before.

'Friend, will your bag ever be full?' said Gwawl.

'It will not,' replied Pwyll, 'unless a great man of power shall press it down with both his feet.'

'Brave sir,' cried Rhiannon to Gwawl, 'rise up and do it.'

At her call, Gwawl rose and put his two feet in the bag and stamped. And then Pwyll pulled up the neck of the bag and slipped the knot tight. He gave a full blast on his horn and his hundred warriors fell on the feast and tied fast the followers of Gwawl. When Pwyll had thrown off his rags and tatters, he ordered each of his men to strike a blow against the bag.

'What have we here?' each cried. 'A badger, a badger,' the others answered. Thus they played with the bag, kicking it and poking it with a staff. 'What is this game?' said one. 'Why, it is the game of Badger in the Bag,' replied the rest.

But Gwawl in his misery cried out, 'My lord, if you can hear me. This is no death for me, to be slain in a bag!'

'True what he says,' added Hefeydd the Old. ''Tis but a mean end, to be slain in a bag.'

'He has had punishment enough,' agreed Rhiannon. 'My lord Pwyll, take a pledge from him that he will never lay claim to me, nor seek vengeance for this.'

'Gladly, gladly I will give it,' came the voice from the bag.

Then Pwyll released Gwawl from the bag, and terms were drawn up and sureties given, as Rhiannon advised.

'Now I am content,' said Pwyll.

'Aye, but I am sore wounded and bruised,' said Gwawl, 'and I have need of a bath. Let me go on my way.'

Then Gwawl departed and the hall was made ready for Pwyll, as it had been the year before. They ate and made merry, and when the time came to sleep Pwyll took Rhiannon to their chamber, and the night was hardly long enough for the pleasure they had of it.

At last, in the new young day, Rhiannon said tenderly, 'Arise, lord, and reward the poets and minstrels. Refuse no one a gift today.'

Each suitor and minstrel was contented, according to the wish of each. And none was denied while the feast lasted. And when the end was reached, Pwyll said to Hefeydd the Old, 'With your permission, I will set out for Dyfed tomorrow.'

'God speed to you,' said Hefeydd. 'Appoint an hour when Rhiannon may follow you.'

'Between me and God,' replied Pwyll, 'we shall go hence together.'

So they travelled in the morn to the court of Arberth, and more gladness and feasting awaited them there. The foremost lords and ladies of the land came to them, and none left Rhiannon without a mark of goodwill – a gift of a brooch, or a ring, or a precious stone. And Pwyll and Rhiannon governed the land well and prosperously, that year and for many a year.

THE STRUGGLE WITHIN
THE HOUSE OF MATH

Math, son of Mathonwy, was lord over Gwynedd, and Pryderi, son of Pwyll, was lord over one-and-twenty counties in the south. And at that time Math might not live except he had his two feet in the fold of a maiden's lap. Now the maiden who was with him was Goewin, daughter of Pebin, and she was the fairest maiden of her time.

Math had two nephews, Gilfaethwy and Gwydion, the sons of Don, and these two lads lusted after Goewin. To get to her chamber, they devised a quarrel between Pryderi and Math. They stole from Pryderi the hogs that came from the underworld of Annwn, and when Math went to claim those hogs the sons of Don found Goewin alone. At Caer Dathyl, Gilfaethwy and the maiden Goewin were put in the bed of Math, and that night she was lain with against her will.

Then there was war between Pryderi and the sons of Don, over the theft of the hogs. In the course of the campaign, Gwydion and Pryderi agreed to meet in single combat, body to body, and by strength and magic Gwydion slew Pryderi. In the land above Y Felenrhyd, Pryderi was buried, and his grave is there.

When Math returned to Caer Dathyl, he sent for his maiden that he might put his feet in the fold of her lap. Goewin came but she said, 'Lord, seek another maiden to be under your feet. I am a woman now.'

'How is that?' he asked.

'An open assault was made upon me, lord, by your sister's sons. They did rape upon me and dishonour on you, and this was in your own chamber and bed.'

'As for them, my nephews,' said Math, 'I will have redress for you and revenge for me. As for you, I will make you my wife, and my realm I will give into your hands.'

Then a ban was made against the sons of Don, that none should give them meat or drink, and at last this forced them to come to Math.

'Lord,' said they, 'we are here at your will.'

'My dishonour you cannot make good to me,' said Math, 'let alone the death of Pryderi. But I will begin a punishment on you.'

Then Math struck them both with his magic wand, so that one became a stag and the other a hind.

'Go together and be coupled,' he said. 'Act like beasts and give birth as they do. And in a year from today return to me.'

A year went past, and on the appointed day there was an uproar of dogs beneath the wall. Then three beasts appeared – a stag, a hind, and a fawn. Math took his wand again and touched two of the beasts, turning the stag into a boar and the hind into a sow. But the fawn he changed into a boy whom he kept and fostered.

And so it happened, in the next two years, that Gwydion and Gilfaethwy, first in the form of hogs and then of wolves, brought forth two more sons whom Math kept and cherished. Then Math thought that the sons of Don had been punished enough, and he changed them with his wand back into their own flesh.

'Make them ready a bath,' said Math, 'and have their heads washed. And now, my nephews, you have had great shame, that you have coupled like beasts and brought forth young. Soon I shall offer you peace and friendship, but tell me first, what maiden shall I now seek?'

'It is easy to answer,' replied Gwydion. 'Aranrhod, daughter of Don, your sister's daughter, is the maiden for you.'

When the girl was fetched, Math summoned her and ordered her to step over his wand, to see if she were truly maiden. But as she did so, there was a loud infant squall and she dropped a fine boy-child with rich yellow hair. After the loud cry she rushed for the door, but some other small thing dropped from her. In a moment, Gwydion snatched it up and wrapped it in a sheet of silk and hid it in a chest at the foot of his bed.

Math was left with the yellow-haired boy whom he baptized and gave the name of Dylan. At once, Dylan made for the sea and went into it and received the sea's nature. He swam as well as any fish, and for this reason he was called Dylan, Son of the Wave.

Some time after, when Gwydion was in his bed, he heard a small weak cry from the chest at the foot of the bed. He opened it and saw little arms thrusting from the silk sheet. When he saw it was a baby boy, Gwydion gave him to be nursed to a woman who had milk, and at once the boy grew wonderfully. In one year he was as big as a two-year-old. The child stayed in the house of Gwydion and came to love him, and he became a sturdy lad always twice as big as another of his own age.

One day, when the two of them were walking, they came by Caer Aranrhod. When the lady had come out to greet them and they had talked, she asked Gwydion, 'What is the boy that goes with you?'

'This boy is your son,' said Gwydion.

'Alas, man,' said she, 'why do you pursue my shame and remind me of it? But what is the boy's name?'

'Faith, there is as yet no name on him.'

'Nor shall he have one,' said Aranrhod, 'till he get it from me. And I will swear on him a destiny.'

'Wicked woman,' cried Gwydion, 'you are angry with him because he made a question of your maidenhood. But never again shall you be called maiden"

The two went away and Gwydion plotted how to get the better of Aranrhod. He made a magic and put it upon himself and the boy. They appeared as shoemakers and sailed in a ship into the lee of the wall at Caer Aranrhod. Aranrhod was pleased to have new shoes. The boy began to measure her foot but then he saw a wren alight in the rigging. He took an aim and hit the little bird between the sinew and the bone of the leg.

'Faith,' laughed Aranrhod, 'the fair youth has hit it with a deft hand.'

'Now he has a name,' cried Gwydion at once, 'and a good one too. Let him be called Lleu Llaw Gyffes, that is to say Fair Deft Hand.'

Then the ship vanished away into the seaweed from which it had been formed, and Aranrhod saw again Gwydion and her son.

'He is named,' she said, 'but he shall never bear arms till I myself equip him.'

Gwydion reared the boy till he could ride any horse and was perfect in all exercises of the body. But he could see that the youth pined for arms. Once more they went to Caer Aranrhod, but this time in the guise of bards from Morgannwg.

'God's welcome to bards, now and always' cried Aranrhod.

In they went, and in the hall there was great joy at their coming and good meat and story-telling, for Gwydion was a great teller of tales.

That night, in the closeness of their chamber, Gwydion devised more magic. At dawn, he made it happen that there was a clamour of trumpets and a tumult of armies around the fort. Soon Aranrhod came bursting into their chamber, crying, 'Good sirs, we are in a bad place. I cannot see the colour of the deep for all the ships that swarm upon us. What shall we do?'

'Lady,' said Gwydion, 'there is no other counsel but to close the fort upon us, and to defend as best we can.'

With that, Aranrhod went to collect arms and armour, and when she returned Gwydion told her to assist in the arming of the youth, which she gladly did.

'Is the arming of that youth completed?' he asked.

'It is,' she said.

'Then we may now doff our arms, for we have no need of them. That fleet was raised by magic, to break your destiny concerning your son and to get him arms. And now he has them.'

'Wicked man,' she said, 'many a good youth might have lost his life in this mustering. So I will swear another destiny on this son. He will get no wife of the race that is now on the earth.'

When he heard this, Gwydion went to Math and made the most sustained complaint in the world against Aranrhod.

'Well,' replied Math, 'let us seek, you and I, by our enchantment and magic to conjure a wife for him out of flowers.'

Now, by this time Lleu Llaw Gyffes had become big in stature, as large as any man, and the handsomest youth ever seen. So Math and Gwydion took the flowers of the oak and the broom and the meadowsweet, and they conjured forth the fairest of maidens with the best of figures. And they called this maiden Blodeuedd, or Flower. Then the two young folk were brought together, and each was pleasing to the eye of the other. They talked and feasted and slept together. For their support, Math gave them good land and territory. They settled there and governed it, and all the people were content with their rule.

One time, when they were visiting Caer Dathyl, the chieftain Gronw Bebyr rode by hunting the stag. He chased long and hard, but as the night fell he was far from home and he went to the fort for lodging. That day, her husband Lleu had departed, but Blodeuedd out of charity came herself with a welcome for Gronw. The chieftain washed and changed and combed well his hair and went to sit with the lady. She looked upon him, and at that moment there was no part of her that was not filled with love. He gazed on her, and his heart was struck to the same degree, and they could not conceal it. Then their talk was all of joy and love, and before the night was old they had embraced. In the dark, they fled to a chamber and slept together.

Then they secretly took counsel how to remain together.

'There is no other way,' said Gronw, 'than this: you must learn from him how his death may be brought about. But do it underhand, in pretence of loving care for him.'

When Gronw departed and her husband returned, Blodeuedd greeted him most gladly, but when they went to bed she put a black look on her face.

'What has befallen you?' he asked. 'Are you not well?'

'I am troubled by the thought of your death,' said she, 'if you should die sooner than I.'

'God repay your loving care,' he said, 'but it is not easy to slay me.'

'Then for God's sake tell me the way. For my memory is a surer safeguard than yours, that we might scheme to avoid this death.'

'I will tell you gladly. The spear that kills me must be a year in the making, working only when folk are at Mass on Sunday. And I shall be slain neither within nor without a house, nor on horseback nor on foot.

'How, then,' she asked, 'may it come about?'

'In this way. Make a bath for me on the river bank, tightly vaulted over by a thatched frame. Bring a he-goat and set it beside the bath. Then if I shall be caught standing with one foot on the goat and one on the edge of the bath, whoever smites me will kill me.'

'I thank God for that,' said Blodeuedd, 'for all of this is most easily avoided.'

At once, she took this news to Gronw, and he laboured for a year in the making of the spear and in getting all things ready on the banks of the Cynfael river. Bath and thatched frame were prepared and a he-goat tethered nearby. Then Blodeuedd begged Lleu Llaw Gyffes to show her, for their greater security, just how the act might be done.

So in an evil hour he went into the bath, and when he was cleansed he stepped from it with a foot on the rim and a foot on the goat, and then Gronw loosed the spear with deadly aim. The shaft stood out from his side but the head of the spear stayed in him. With a loud scream Lleu flew up in the form of an eagle and vanished. Then the lovers were free for each other, and they subdued the land and ruled it.

Math, son of Mathonwy, heard this news with grief, and the sorrow of Gwydion was even greater. Very soon, Gwydion set out to seek that eagle. He travelled the length and breadth of the land till he came by chance to a house in Arfon where a swineherd was relating the strange journeys of his sow.

'Every day,' said the man, 'when the sty is open, out she goes, so fast that no one can keep in touch with her. It is as if she disappears into the earth.'

'For my sake,' said Gwydion, 'do this. Do not open the sty till I am prepared and ready to follow her.'

It was easily done, and then when the sow leapt forth Gwydion was after her. She went fast up the valley, but after a while she stopped and began to feed, and Gwydion could see that she fed on rotten flesh and maggots. He looked into the top of a tree and saw an eagle shaking maggots and flesh onto the ground. Gwydion thought that this eagle might be Lleu Llaw Gyffes, so he sang three verses of a powerful song and enticed the eagle down from the tree.

The eagle hopped down painfully and alighted on Gwydion's knee. Then Gwydion touched it with his wand and the bird took on human form again. Yet no one had ever seen anything as pitiful as this man. It was Lleu Llaw Gyffes and he was nothing but thin skin and out-sticking bones.

He was brought to Caer Dathyl and good doctors tended him, and before a year was out he was whole again. Then he lusted for revenge. He mustered a band of warriors, and they set out grimly after Gronw and Blodeuedd. When Blodeuedd heard them coming, she fled away with her maidens into the mountains. But as they ran, in their fear they looked ever backwards, and thus they stumbled into a lake where all were drowned except Blodeuedd.

While she was recovering on the bank, Gwydion and his men galloped to her, and Gwydion's face was like the thundercloud.

'I will not slay you,' he cried, 'but I will do worse. You shall be changed into the form of a bird. But for fear of other birds you will not dare to show your face to the light, and there will be enmity between you and all other birds. They will mob you and molest you wherever they see you. No longer shall you be Blodeuedd the Flower, but you shall be Blodeuwedd the Owl.'

As his lady had been taken and humbled, Gronw sued for peace. He offered reparation for injury, either land or gold or silver.

'By my faith, I will not accept any of that,' said Lleu. 'But I shall aim a spear at you in the manner that you aimed at me, and that is the best I shall offer you.'

'Well, let it be thus,' said Gronw sadly. But then he suddenly cried out, 'My men and foster-brothers, is there none of you that will take the blow for me?'

'Faith, there is none,' they all cried. And so Gronw could not avoid the blow.

They came to the bank of the Cynfael river and all was prepared as before. Gronw got up in the place between the bath and the goat and then said to Lleu, 'Lord, since a woman's wiles deceived me, I beg you let me set a stone between me and the blow.'

This request was granted. Gronw took a large stone from the bank and held it in front of his breast. But the spear of Lleu pierced right through the stone and the man. His back was cut asunder and Gronw was slain. And the stone is still there, on the bank of the river, with a hole through it.

Then Lleu Llaw Gyffes regained his Land, and he ruled prosperously over all of Gwynedd.

159

CULHWCH
AND OLWEN

When Cilydd took to himself a wife, the country prayed that the couple might have offspring. Through these prayers, the wife grew big with child, but she went mad and wandered far from house and home. So when her time was upon her, she was in a wild place where a swineherd was keeping pigs. Through terror of these pigs the queen was delivered. The swineherd took the boy and named him Culhwch, because he was found in a pig-run. But this child was of good and gentle birth, being first cousin to Arthur.

After the birth, the mother of the child continued to fail, and she said to her husband, 'My death is near, and then you shall wish for another wife. Wives bring many gifts. But do not despoil your son. For my sake, take no wife till you see a two-headed briar on my grave.'

The king promised this, and then the queen died. After a time, the king sent each morning to the grave, to see what was growing there. But before she died the queen had secretly ordered a servant to keep the grave stripped of growth. And the grave was bare for seven years till this man neglected his duty. One day, when the king was out hunting, he saw a briar on the grave, and then he wished for a wife. He asked his counsellors what woman would suit him. They answered that the wife of King Doged would be best for him. So Cilydd attacked Doged, slew him, took his wife and daughter, and possessed his land.

Culhwch grew up away from the court and it was a long time before the new queen learnt of her step-son. Then she chided her husband and had him bring her step-son to court. She saw that he was a bold brave youth.

'It were well for you to take a wife,' she said to Culhwch, 'and I have a daughter worthy of any nobleman.'

'But I am not yet of age to take a wife,' said Culhwch.

'Then I will swear a destiny upon you,' replied the queen. 'Your body will never lie against woman till you win Olwen, the daughter of Ysbaddaden, Chief Giant.'

The youth flushed red, and love of that maiden entered into every bit of his body, though he had never seen her. At once, he went to his father.

'My step-mother has sworn on me,' he said, 'that I needs must win Olwen, daughter of Ysbaddaden, Chief Giant.'

'It is not difficult,' replied the king. 'Arthur is your first cousin. Go to Arthur to trim your hair, and ask a gift of him.'

Off went Culhwch on a grey horse, and not the tip of his sleeve fluttered, so lightly did the horse step. The boy had a sword at his side and a battle-axe in his hand, sharp enough to cut the wind.

'Is there a porter here?' Culhwch called at Arthur's gate.

'There is, and the head lies uneasy on those who ask. I am porter each first day of January, and then there are others. One goes on his head to spare his feet, like a rolling stone on a hard floor.'

'Open the gate,' cried Culhwch.

'That I will not. There is a throng in the hall, knife has gone into meat, and drink into horn. Now, save for a craftsman or the son of a king, none may enter. But in the hospice you may have food enough for fifty men. Meat for your dogs, corn for your horse, hot peppered chops for yourself. Also wine brimming over, and delectable songs, and a woman for your bed. And tomorrow, when the gate is open, you shall sit where you like in Arthur's hall, high or low.'

'I will do nothing of that,' replied Culhwch. 'If you do not open, I will give three shouts at the entrance, no less audible in Cornwall than in the depths of the north or in Ireland. And every woman bearing child will miscarry, and those not with child shall have a stone in the womb.'

'Shout as much as you like,' said the porter, 'but wait here till I have a word with Arthur.'

The porter went into Arthur and said, 'I have seen at the gate many fair kingly men, but never one so comely as the one now there.'

'Well,' replied Arthur, 'you have entered walking but go out running. It is a shameful thing to leave one such as that in the wind and rain.'

'Nay, sir,' said Cei, who was listening, 'the laws of this court should not be broken.'

'Not so, fair Cei,' said Arthur. 'We are noble men only so long as our folk call to us. The greater our bounty, the greater our nobility and fame and glory.'

Then Culhwch was brought in, and he saluted the king and the company.

'O king,' he said, 'I come here not to beg meat and drink. If I ask a boon, I will repay it, and I will praise it. I will carry your renown to the four corners of the world.'

'Fair youth,' replied Arthur, 'you shall have your boon as far as the wind drives, the rain wets, the sun runs, and the sea stretches.'

'God's truth thereon?'

'Gladly. Name your request.'

'I will,' said Culhwch. 'I would have my hair trimmed.'

Then Arthur took silver shears and a golden comb and trimmed him.

'Tell me your name and ask what you wish,' said Arthur, 'for my heart grows tender towards you.'

'I am Culhwch, son of Cilydd, and I wish that you would get me Olwen, daughter of Ysbaddaden, Chief Giant. I invoke her in the name of your warriors.'

But Arthur had never heard of this maiden, nor could his messengers find her.

After a time, when they had looked far and wide, Culhwch said, 'Everyone has obtained his boon, yet I am still lacking. I will go away and take your honour with me.'

'Be not so hasty,' said Cei, 'and come with us. If she exists in this world, we will not part from you till we find her.'

Arthur called on his best men to go with Cei. First was one-handed Bedwyr, who could still spill blood in the battle better than any three warriors. Then there was Cynddylig the Guide, and after him came Gwrhyr, Interpreter of Tongues, and Gwalchmei the Walker and Menw the Caster of Spells.

Away they went, travelling far across a wide open plain till they saw a fort in the distance. They could also see a great flock of sheep without limit or end. And a shepherd in skins was attending them, with a shaggy mastiff bigger than a nine-year-old stallion. Never a lamb had this shepherd lost, much less a grown beast. No man could pass the shepherd without deadly hurt, and his breath seared black the dead trees and bushes.

'Interpreter of Tongues,' said Cei, 'approach yonder fellow and have words with him.'

'It is safer to go all together,' said Menw. 'And have no fear, for I will put a spell on the dog.'

So they went forward to speak to the shepherd.

'The world goes well with you, shepherd?' said they.

'As well with me as with you,' he replied. 'There is no affliction to do me harm save my wife.'

'Whose sheep are these, and whose fort?'

'Are you fools? All the world knows that this is the fort of Ysbaddaden, Chief Giant.'

'And you, who are you?'

'I am Custennin the Shepherd, and because of my wife the Chief Giant has wrought my ruin. But who are you?'

'We are messengers from Arthur, come to seek Olwen.'

'Ho, men, God protect you! Never a man has asked that and gone away with his life.'

Then Culhwch gave Custennin a gold ring, so that he might be a friend to them. And when the shepherd's wife saw this ring, she knew that the Culhwch, son of Cilydd, who had arrived was her own sister's son. And she was sad because his quest for Olwen made his life in danger.

The travellers were taken to the shepherd's house, and then the wife opened a coffer in which was hidden a little lad with curly yellow hair.

''Tis a pity to hide a lad like that,' said Gwrhyr.

'He is the only one left,' said she. 'Three and twenty of my sons have been killed by Ysbaddaden, Chief Giant, and I have no more hope for this one than the others. But God protect you, how will you win your way to Olwen?'

'Is there a place where we may see her privately?'

'Every Saturday, she comes here to wash her head,' replied the wife, 'and all her rings she leaves in the bowl. But I will not betray one who trusts me. Only if you pledge her no harm will I send for her.'

That promise was given, and Olwen came, with a robe of flame-red silk about her. Her hair was more yellow than the flower of broom, and her flesh whiter than the foam of water. Her eye was brighter than the eye of a falcon, and her breast fairer than that of the white swan. Whoever beheld her was filled with love for her. White trefoils grew in her path, and for that reason she was called Olwen.

When she came and sat in the shepherd's house, Culhwch knew her at once. His heart went out to her and he said, 'Ah maiden, 'tis you I have loved. Now come with me.'

'It would be my sin if I did so,' said Olwen. 'I cannot go without my father's consent, for his life will end when I get a husband. But go and ask my father. However much he demands from you, promise to give it, and then you shall have me too.'

She took them to her father's fort where the gates were down and the men on guard. Nine men were killed at the gates without a sound, and nine mastiffs without one squealing. Then the messengers of Arthur went to the hall.

'In the name of God and men,' they cried, 'greetings unto you, Chief Giant! We have come to seek Olwen, your daughter, for Culhwch son of Cilydd.'

'Where are my rascally servants?' roared the giant. 'Raise up the forks under my two eyelids that I may see my future son-in-law.'

That was done and he had a good look. Then he said, 'Come again tomorrow and I'll give you some kind of answer.'

But as they rose to leave, Ysbaddaden, Chief Giant, snatched up a poisoned spear and hurled it after them. Bedwyr caught it, hurled it back, and pierced the giant through the ball of the knee.

'Cursed savage son-in-law,' he cried. 'Now I shall walk the worse up a slope. The poisoned iron has pained me like the sting of a gadfly.'

Next day, they came again with pomp and brave combs in their hair to demand the daughter of the giant. He asked for more time to take counsel, but again as they were leaving he threw a second spear. Menw hurled it back, and it pierced the giant through and through, coming out at the small of his back.

'Cursed savage son-in-law,' he roared again. 'The hard iron has pained me like the bite of a big-headed leech. When I go uphill I shall have tightness of chest, and belly-ache, and a frequent loathing of meat.'

On the third day they begged the giant to throw no more spears. But still he grabbed one and threw it. Culhwch hurled it back, and it pierced the giant through the ball of the eye and came out of the nape of the neck.

'Cursed savage son-in-law,' he roared again. 'The iron has wounded me like the bite of a mad dog. So long as I am alive, my sight will be the worse. My eyes will water against the wind, and I shall have headache and giddiness each new moon.'

But on the next day the messengers said roughly, 'Shoot no more. Seek not deadly hurt and martyrdom, or you may get worse. Give us your daughter.'

'Who seeks her?' asked the giant.

''Tis I, Culhwch, son of Cilydd.'

'Give me what I shall name to you, then you shall have my daughter.'

'Then name what you wish.'

Ysbaddaden, Chief Giant, began to name the many hard things that he wanted for the celebration of a wedding and a feast, and a myriad of things were these indeed.

'See that great thicket yonder?' the giant began. 'All in one day it must be uprooted and burnt and ploughed and manured and sown, so that the crop will be ripe in the morning against the drying of the dew, in order that the feast may be cooked for my daughter and my guests.'

'That is easy for me,' replied Culhwch, 'though you think it not easy.'

'There is more,' went on the giant. 'Fetch the man to till the land. He will not come of his own will, nor can you force him.'

'That is easy for me,' said Culhwch, 'though you think it not easy.'

'There is more. Bring the man to the headland, to form and make the iron plough. He will not willingly work, nor can you compel him.'

'That is easy for me, though you think it not easy.'

'There is more. Yoke two oxen together to plough the rough ground, and one ox is on this side and the other is in Scotland. And though all this you might get, there are things you will not get.'

'That is easy for me,' said Culhwch again, 'though you think it not easy.'

'But there is more, and many things more,' said the Chief Giant. 'For the proper conduct of the feast I must have nine measures of flax seed sown. I must have honey sweeter than that of a virgin swarm. The drinking-cup of Llwyr. The food-hamper of Gwyddneu. The serving-horn of Gwlgwad. The harp of Teirtu. And the birds of Rhiannon that wake the dead and lull the living to sleep.'

'That is easy for me, though you think it not easy.'

'But listen further. I must have the Irishman's cauldron to wash my head, and the tusk of the Chief Boar to shave me, and the blood of the Black Witch to dress my beard, and the vessel of the Dwarf to keep the blood in.'

Thus on and on went the Chief Giant, piling difficult thing on more difficult thing. Yet to everything Culhwch only replied, 'That is easy for me, though you think it not easy.'

'No sleep at night and wakefulness,' said Ysbaddaden, Chief Giant, 'shall you have in seeking all those things. And still you will not get them, nor will you get my daughter.'

'I have horses and horsemen,' replied Culhwch, 'and my lord and kinsman Arthur will get me all those things. I shall win your daughter, and you shall lose your life.'

With that, the messengers left the fort of the Chief Giant and returned to the court of Arthur and told him how it had gone with them. Arthur offered his own help, but after the first task had been done, the men said to him, 'Lord, get you home. It is not worthy of you to seek things as petty as these.'

So Arthur went no more but sent his men on the quest with many kind words.

The men took counsel together and decided to begin their quest with the search for the huntsman, Mabon, son of Modron. When three nights old, he was taken from his mother and no one knew where he was, or whether he was alive or dead.

After long searching, Mabon was found and rescued from his prison. Thus the quest was well begun. As they went on over the Three Realms of Britain, and even into Ireland, one by one they accomplished what Ysbaddaden, Chief Giant, had imposed on them, and at last they returned to Arthur's court.

'What marvel is still to be done?' he asked.

'There is one,' they replied. 'We have yet to fetch the blood of the Black Witch from the Valley of Grief in the uplands of Hell.'

Now this was a task worthy of Arthur, so this time he set out with them. They found the hag and attacked her in her cave. But she caught the servants of the king by the hair of the head and threw them down and disarmed them. Then she drove them out squealing. Arthur was angry to see his servants well-nigh killed. He wanted to grapple the hag with his own hands, but his men stopped him.

'It is not seemly or pleasant,' said they, 'to see you scuffling with an old hag. Let your servants deal with her.'

More servants entered the cave but they fared as badly as the others. And God knows, not one of them would have left that place whole had not each one been loaded on Llamrei, Arthur's own mare. Then Arthur himself entered the cave and threw his great knife at the hag. It struck her across the middle and separated her in two, as if she were two tubs. At once, Cadw of Prydein caught up the witch's blood, and they all fled away from that dire place.

When all the marvels had been collected together, Culhwch took them to the court of the Chief Giant. With him were the son of Custennin and all those others who had reason to hate Ysbaddaden, Chief Giant. The giant demanded the performance of all the promises made to him. One of the tasks was to shave the giant with the tusk of the Chief Boar. Cadw was the man to do the shaving, and as he did so he cut flesh and skin to the bone and took off the giant's two ears outright.

'Is that shave enough for you, man?' asked Culhwch.

'It is,' said the giant.

'Is your daughter now mine?'

'Yours indeed,' said Ysbaddaden, Chief Giant. 'Do not thank me for her. It is Arthur who has secured her for you. You would never have gained her alone. And now it is the time to take away my life.'

So the son of Custennin, the little lad who had been

hidden in the chest, took the giant by the hair and dragged him to the mound of the fort. Then he cut off the head and set it on a stake on the battlements, and the son of the shepherd took possession of the fort and the lands of the Chief Giant.

That night, Culhwch and Olwen slept together, and she was his only wife for as long as he lived.

MIDIR AND ETAIN

Midir was from the hill of the *shee* in Bri Leith and he had a wife called Fuamnach. But his heart went towards Etain and he married her also, to the great jealousy of his first wife. Fuamnach asked the help of the druid Bresal, and he put a spell on Etain and drove her out of her own house.

The wind caught her up and whirled her away to Angus Og, the son of the Dagda, and he kept Etain and nourished her. He made a bright house for her, with clear windows, and filled it with the scent of flowers, and she could see out but none could see in. After a time, Fuamnach heard that Etain was safe and well, and this made her hatred grow stronger. She went to the bright glass house when Angus was away. Then with more druid spells she turned Etain into a butterfly, and she raised such a blast of wind that Etain was thrown high and far across the sky.

For seven years the wind buffeted Etain about till she was blown into a house in Ulster where the men of Inver Cichmany were feasting. From a beam of the roof she fell into a gold cup that was beside the wife of Etar. The woman drank her down with the wine, and at the end of nine months Etain was re-born from the womb of Etar.

Then this new child grew up in the house of Etar with fifty maidens about her, and she was well fed and well clothed. On a certain day, when all the girls were bathing in the bay of Cichmany, they saw a rider with very high looks coming towards the water. He was on a big bay horse with a curly mane and a flowing tail. A green cloak was about him, and his shirt was embroidered with red-gold thread. A shield of silver rested on his back, and his spear had rings of gold from shaft to head. Fair yellow hair he had, drawn back from his forehead with a braid of gold.

'Etain is here,' he called, 'by the Hill of Fair Women. among the children at play. O Etain, for your sake Eochaid of Meath will fight many battles. War will come to the *shee*, and thousands will suffer.'

After he had spoken he vanished, and no one knew where he went.

Now, while Etain was growing to womanhood, Eochaid was High-king of Ireland. At this time, he ordered a feast at Tara and invited the men of Ireland there to make their tribute.

'We will not come,' they answered, 'during such time, long or short, that the king of Ireland remains without a worthy wife. For among our noble men there can be none who is wifeless, and no king without a queen. Nor does any man go to the feast without his lady.'

So Eochaid sent messengers to search all the land for a maiden girl worthy to be queen. Soon they returned and told the king of the girl at Inver Cichmany, beautiful beyond all others.

The king set out to see her, and as he rode over the green at Bri Leith he saw a fair woman letting down her hair to wash it, with a golden basin by her side. Her arms coming out of her smock were as white as the new night snow, and her cheeks were as rosy as the foxglove. Her eyes were blue as hyacinth, her lips crimson, and her teeth like pearls. The brightness of the moon was in her face, high pride on her forehead, and the light of wooing in her eyes.

The desire of her seized upon the king and he said, 'Maiden, who are you?'

'Easy to tell,' she replied. 'I am Etain, daughter of the king of Echrad. Twenty years have I grown by the magic mounds of the *shee*, and their kings from below have been wooing me. But never one of them has slept with me. 'Tis for you I have come here. I have heard such high tales of your looks and splendour that I have come to love you. I will be yours. Pay whatever bride-price befits me, and after that let my desire for you be fulfilled.'

Eochaid paid her bride-price and took her to Tara where a fair and hearty welcome was made for her.

It was the feast of Samhain, at summer's end, and for a fortnight there was good eating and drinking. Ailill, brother to Eochaid, was at the court for the festival. He was also called Anglonach, for he had Only One Fault. When Ailill saw Etain, his brother's fair wife, he could not look away.

'What far thing are you gazing at?' said his wife. 'Such long looks are a sign of love.'

At this, Ailill turned colour in his face and looked no more. But he could not forget what he had seen and he became sick with desire and envy.

For a year, Ailill grew pale and thin, then his brother Eochaid came to him and put his hand on his breast.

'Brother, how fares it with you?' he said.

'I am not any easier,' said Ailill, 'but worse day and night. I cannot say what ails me.'

So the king sent Fachtna, his own doctor, who came and listened to Ailill's heart.

'This sickness will not kill you,' said Fachtna, 'for I know it well. It comes from the pangs of envy, or the pangs of love, and you have not found a way out of it.'

When he heard this, Ailill was shamed and would not confess himself to the doctor, so Fachtna left him.

Soon after this time, Eochaid went on a visit of all the provinces of his realm. As he was still worried about the health of his brother, he said to Etain, 'Fair lady, while I am away care for Ailill gently so long as he lives, and make a grave in the sod for him if he dies. Raise a stone over the grave and write his name on it in Ogham.'

Then Eochaid left for the space of a year. And Etain dealt tenderly with Ailill. Often they talked together, and when she saw that he got no better she sang for him and then said, 'Fair youth, whose step was once so strong, what ails you? You are wasting in bed, yet the sun still shines.'

'There is good reason for it,' he replied. 'My joy is gone, my harp no longer pleases, my lips turn away from food.'

'Tell me, you poor man, of your trouble. I am wise and may help you.'

'My words would choke me. Woman-secrets are best hidden.'

'If there is one among the fair faces of Ireland who torments you so, I myself will woo her to come to your side.'

'Woman,' replied Ailill, 'you yourself can put this sickness from me. A love, as long as a year, holds closer to me than my skin, and its strength is stronger than wrath. It shakes my world into four pieces.'

Then Etain stood rooted, for she saw now what his sickness was, and it was a heavy trouble to her. But she still tended to him, and brought him food, and poured water over his hands, for it was a grief to her that he should pine away for her sake. And on a certain day she came to him early and said, 'Rise-up, Ailill, son of a king.'

Then she threw arms about him and kissed him and said further, 'I will heal you. Come at the break of day to the house outside the fort, and I shall give you all you desire.'

That night, Ailill struggled with sleep, but close by the dawn he slept soundly at last, well into the day. Etain went to the place of meeting, and at the right hour she saw a weary sick man coming slowly towards her. But when he came close she saw it was not Ailill. Then the man went away and she returned to the fort.

Ailill woke at mid-morning, and when he knew he had missed his meeting he would rather have had death than life. But Etain soothed him with words, and they made another tryst for the next morning.

The same thing happened on the second, and on the third day. But on that day Etain spoke to the strange man.

'It is not you I come to meet,' she said. 'Why are you here? The man I would meet, I come to him not from desire or fear but to cure him from the sickness he has caught from the love of me.'

'It is more fitting for you to meet me,' said the stranger, 'than any other man. Long ago, I was your husband and your first man.'

'What thing are you saying?' she cried. 'And what name have you in this land?'

'That is easy to tell. I am Midir of Bri Leith.'

'And what made you part from me, if it was as you say?'

'It was the jealousy of Fuamnach and the sorcery of Bresal the druid that drove us apart. And now, Etain, will you come with me?'

'I will not,' she said. 'What sense is it to give up the high-king of Ireland for a man unknown to me and of unknown kindred?'

'It was I myself,' said Midir, 'who filled the mind of Ailill with love for you. And it was I who stopped him from meeting you, to keep your honour whole.'

Then Etain returned to the house of Ailill and told him all that had happened. When he heard this, Ailill was cured of both his sickness and his desire.

'It has fallen well for both of us,' said he, 'for I am cured in body and mind, and you are unhurt in your honour.'

'Thanks be to all our gods,' she replied, 'for this blessing upon us.'

Soon after, Eochaid came back from his journey. He saw that his brother was cured, and he praised Etain for the good deeds she had done for Ailill's health.

Now, in the summer of that year Eochaid the king was at Tara. He was looking over the Plain of Breg, a place beautiful in its colour, and excellent as to blossom, with all manner of growing things. Then he saw a strange young warrior approaching, and this was the very same high handsome rider that appeared before, when the girls of Inver Cichmany were swimming in the bay.

'I give you welcome,' said Eochaid, 'though to me you are as yet unknown. Declare yourself.'

'A good greeting,' replied the stranger, 'but in truth I know you well. My own name is nothing very great. I am Midir of Bri Leith. I have come to play a game of chess with you.'

'Truly, I am skilful at chess-play,' said the king. 'But the chessboard is in the house, and Etain is asleep there at this time.'

But Midir produced his own silver board set with precious stones, and his own chessmen of gold. He set out the pieces and said, 'What stake shall rest on the game?'

The first game was played for fifty grey horses. Midir held back his hand, so the king won and Midir paid the stake. They played again and the king won, and this time he gave Midir a hard task. He was to clear rocks and stones from the plains of Meath, and reeds from the lands of Tethba, and trees from the forest of Breg, and lastly to build a causeway across the bog of Lamrach.

Midir summoned his people of the *shee* from Bri Leith, and even though they had the powers of magic there were still hard days enough for them in the doing of all these things. Eochaid was out at the daybreak watching them, and he saw that the folk of the *shee* yoked their oxen at the shoulder and not by a strap over the forehead, as used to be done. Then the king taught this way to his own farmers, and for this he gained the title of Eochaid Airem, that is to say Eochaid of the Plough.

Thin and weak was Midir after all this work, but he came to Eochaid to play a third game of chess. They played, and this time Midir did not hold back his hand.

'The stake this time,' said he, 'it is Etain your wife.'

'That shall not be,' said the king.

'Then let me put my arms about her and kiss her but once,'

said Midir. This was agreed, and a time was set for the end of the month.

On the appointed day Midir came back to Tara and stood in the hall as handsome a man as ever was seen. The champions of Ireland, ring upon ring, stood guard around the fort, and the king and the queen were in the midst of their house, with the outer courtyard shut and locked. It would be a hard fight to break in or out.

'I have come to be paid,' said Midir. 'Etain is the price due to me.'

When Etain heard this she changed colour and was ashamed. But Midir said to her, 'Let there be no shame on you, Etain, for I have sought your love through the length of a year. You have refused my riches and my treasure and my body till such time as your husband would give you leave.'

'That is spoken truly,' said Etain. 'Now what says my husband?'

'You shall not go,' said Eochaid. 'He shall have only as much as I promised, that is to say one kiss with his arms around you.'

Midir took his sword in his left hand and the woman beneath his right shoulder, and he kissed her. The warriors of the king closed in on them and made a rush for them, but Midir lifted Etain as lightly as a spider's web and they flew up through the skylight of the house and out into the air. The champions of Ireland gazed up but could not follow. What they saw was a pair of swans steadily beating the air with great wings, joined by a slender gold chain.

In his anger, Eochaid searched for them throughout all Ireland. But nothing was heard of them, for they were safe under the hills, in the dwellings of the *shee*.

THE SONS OF
USNECH

Fedlimid, son of Dall, was harper and bard to
Conchobor the king, and the men of Ulster listened to
his tales. On a certain day Fedlimid was speaking, and
the men were in their cups, and the wife of the bard stood
by the board to serve them. She was big with child. At
the end of the feast, when the men went fuddled to
bed, the wife of Fedlimid wished also to sleep. But as she
went through the silent house her child cried in the womb,
and the cry went to every chamber so that men sprang up
in alarm. The woman was brought before the company and
Fedlimid spoke to her.

'What is that cry,' he said, 'torn from the womb by terror
and hurt? My heart is full of foreboding.'

The woman turned away, having no words to say, and went
to the druid Cathbad for the help of his secret knowledge.

177

'O druid,' she said, 'I know nothing of that cry from within me. The understanding of woman enters not into the womb.'

Cathbad laid his hand on the body of the woman and felt the baby stir within.

'It is indeed a girl-child who is there,' he said. 'Deirdre shall be her name, and sorrow shall be upon her. Blood shall be shed for her, and the light of many bright heroes of Ireland shall be snuffed out.'

And when the child was born, Cathbad held the baby in his arms and told of her fate.

'O Deirdre,' he sang, 'flame of beauty, fair of face, men shall weep and women wail for the trouble you bring. Pity Ulster, have pity for the angry deeds that shall be done in Emain. In your face I see the shadow of banishment and death. Poor fair child, you shall be a giver of wounds, a cause of blood-letting.'

Then the young men of Ulster cried out. 'Let the babe be slain!'

But Conchobor the king would not have it so.

'This child,' he said, 'shall be reared apart, according to my will. In time, she shall be my wife and the companion of my years.'

Who could stand against the wish of the king? The nurse, Levarcham, took the babe to a place far from eyes and ears. On the wild mountainside a little house was made, by a green hillock, with apple-trees beside it and a wall all around. A roof of green sods covered the house, and none entered there except by the command of Levarcham.

Deirdre grew up without the friendship and meetings of people, wandering alone in the lonely hills. She was as fine a girl as you might see, none prettier, as slim and tall as a rush, as graceful as a swan. She was a friend to all birds and beasts, but the folk of the world she did not know.

On a certain day in winter, when Deirdre was well-grown, she and her woman were walking the hills when they chanced on a hunter, who was skinning an animal. Blood lay on the white snow and a raven poked about for a bit to eat.

'Levarcham,' said Deirdre, 'I see here signs that tell of the only man I shall ever love. He shall have hair as black as a raven, cheeks as red as blood, and a body as white as snow.'

'Good fortune to you, woman,' said the hunter when he heard this. 'There are people beyond the hill who are such as you desire. And the best of these are Naoise and his brothers, the three sons of Usnech.'

'However that may be,' cried Levarcham, 'I'll not thank you for telling it. Get you away on the other road.'

But Deirdre had heard him well, and she said to Levarcham, 'I shall never be in health again till I shall see this Naoise or his brothers.'

Now some time later Naoise, son of Usnech, found himself in the wild, near to the little house where Deirdre lived. Like all of Ulster, Naoise had heard the prophecy of Cathbad, and he knew the intent of the king to marry this girl, so he was ready to pass by on the other side. But Deirdre came from the house and skipped past him as light and quick as a fawn.

'Fair is the young heifer that springs past me,' he called.

'Indeed, young heifers are frisky,' she replied, 'in a place where none may find a bull.'

'Your bull,' he said, 'is the bull of the whole province of Ulster, even Conchobor the king.'

'If I would choose, I would take for myself a younger bull, such a one as you are.'

'Not that, for I fear the prophecy of Cathbad.'

'Say you so?' said Deirdre. 'Do you mean to refuse me?'

'Yes indeed,' said he.

Then she leapt upon him and seized him by his ears and cried, 'Two ears of shame and mockery shall you have unless you take me for your wife.'

'O my wife, release me!" cried Naoise. And she did.

Naoise returned to his two brothers and told them what had happened. When they heard this, the other sons of Usnech hurried to hold back their brother.

'What have you done?' they said. 'Do not stir up war between us and the men of Ulster.'

But Naoise would not undo what had been done.

'Evil will fall upon you,' lamented his brothers, 'and you

shall lie under the reproach of shame for as long as you live. But we will stand by you. Let us flee with her into another place, for there are kings in Ireland who will welcome us still.'

They departed that same night, with three times fifty warriors and their women and dogs and servants. And Deirdre went with them. For a long time they wandered from one court to another, from Ballyshannon in the west to the mountain of Howth in the east. Often Conchobor sent men to kill them, by ambush or by treachery, and the warriors of Ulster chased after the sons of Usnech. In time, their enemies drove them over the sea to Scotland where they lived among the beasts of the wilderness.

Then there came hard times, when hunting failed, and the sons of Usnech raided the cattle of the country, and the men of Scotland met together to destroy them. So the sons of Usnech begged mercy of the king of Scotland. And since they were likely men and good warriors he took them into his following and they fought for him. They built for themselves houses in the meadow a little way distant from the king's court. These houses were set apart for Deirdre's sake. They wished to hide her away, lest men might see her, and kill them for her.

One day the steward of the king was going by the house of Naoise early in the morning. He peeped in the window and saw two heads on one pillow, and he thought the face of the woman in the bed was the fairest ever seen. The steward hurried back to the king and woke him.

'Until this day,' he said, 'we have never found a wife worthy of your fame and dignity. But Naoise, son of Usnech, in his house by the meadow, has a woman sufficient for the emperor of the western world. Let us kill Naoise, and let his woman share your bed.'

'It would be to our shame to kill him,' replied the king. 'But rather go yourself each day to her house and secretly woo her for me.'

Then the steward went with whispers and gifts, but all that he said was repeated by Deirdre to Naoise. When the king saw that he was gaining nothing by this wooing, he sent the sons of Usnech to war, into the most dangerous battles, hoping that they might be killed. But they were too strong and brave to be easily slain. Then the men of Scotland met again to plot their destruction. But this also was told to Deirdre.

'Flee from this place,' she said to Naoise. 'If you are not gone this very night, in the morning you shall be killed.'

So they fled away that night to an island in the sea. And after some time the news of their escape was brought to the land of Ulster.

''Tis pity, O Conchobor,' said the men of Ulster to the king, 'that the sons of Usnech should die for the sake of that woman in the lands of an enemy. If die they must, let it be here in their own sweet country. It is a sorry thing to die among foes.'

Then Conchobor sent messengers and sureties to the sons of Usnech, inviting them to come home.

'Indeed we will come,' they replied. 'It is welcome news. But let the sureties for our well-being be Fergus and Black Dubhtach and Cormac, son of Conchobor.'

Now the sons of Usnech hurried home, for they swore to eat no more meat till they sat at the tables of Ireland. But the sureties were feasting across the sea before they left for home, and this was by the contrivance of Conchobor, who was planning some treachery against the sons of Usnech.

At that same time, Eoghan, son of Durthacht, had come to Emain Macha to make his peace with Conchobor, for the two of them had been enemies for many years. Then the king said to Eoghan, 'The price of peace for you is the death of the sons of Usnech.'

On their journey home, Naoise and his brothers had come to the flat of the meadow that lay before Emain, and the women sat on the battlements ready to welcome them. Fiacha, the son of the surety Fergus, stood with Naoise. Suddenly, Eoghan and his warriors rushed from the gates and bore down on the sons of Usnech. Eoghan himself greeted Naoise with a mighty thrust of his spear through

181

the side. The spear passed through Naoise and broke his back in sunder. At once, Fiacha threw his arms around Naoise and carried him to the ground to try to protect him. But Naoise was utterly slain, even through the body of the son of Fergus.

A general murder followed in all parts of the meadow. The warriors of Eoghan, by the points of their spears and the edges of their swords, did not allow any to escape, except for Deirdre. She was captured and bound tight and taken to Conchobor to be in his power.

When the carnage was over and the green of the field was red with blood, the sureties arrived from their feasting beyond the sea. And when they saw what had been done, in despite of their own honour, they were angry beyond measure. Fergus and Dubhtach and Cormac ran forward to attack the men of Eoghan, and in their wrath they did great deeds. Many of the best in Emain were killed. Even Conchobor could not contain the fire and the heat of the foe. In blind rage Dubhtach slew the women of Ulster, and before the rising of the dawn Fergus had put a blaze to Emain itself.

After this destruction the sureties, even Fergus and Dubhtach and Cormac, son of Conchobor, went into exile, into the land of Connacht to find shelter with Ailill and Maeve. Three thousand men went with them, and these exiles showed no more love to their homeland of Ulster. For sixteen years their raids and forays made men quake, and the cries of lamentation among the people of Ulster did not cease.

When the battle was over, Conchobor took Deirdre into his house and kept her. For a year she made no smile and gave no laugh. She could hardly eat or sleep, and she wept with her head on her knee. By the grave of Naoise she used to lie down, and here she made a lament.

'For half the night I sleep not,' she cried. 'My mind wanders amid clouds of thoughts, I eat not, nor smile. The man under heaven who was fairest to me – so dear a man – has been torn from me. Great was the crime. I shall not see him till I die.

'O Naoise, your absence is the cause of grief to me. I see the shadow of this son of Usnech showing through the dark sod that covers now his white body, a body that I desired above most other things. If King Conchobor and all his warriors stood on this plain, I would give up all of them without a struggle for one more moment in the sweet company of Naoise.'

Conchobor heard this lament, and he went to her and tried to comfort her. But she gave him only sad and bitter words.

'And Conchobor the king, what of you?' she said. 'You have given me only tears and sorrow. Such will be my remaining life, for your love will not last me. O King, soon I shall reach my early grave. Stronger than the sea is my grief – do you not know it, Conchobor?'

Then the king turned away from her and said, 'Who is the worst of those you see and hate?'

'It is yourself,' she answered, 'and with you Eoghan, son of Durthacht.'

'Then I give you to him,' said the king, 'and you shall live with him for a year.'

In the morning Deirdre was placed in a chariot, and she saw that the two men with her were those she hated most upon the earth.

'Ha, Deirdre,' Conchobor mocked her, 'the look you share now between me and Eoghan is the same that the ewe gives between two rams.'

As the chariot ran across the plains of Macha, they came to a place of great bare stones. All at once Deirdre leapt from the speeding chariot and struck her head against a large rock. Then her head was shattered, and so Deirdre died.

THE PURSUIT
OF DIARMUID AND
GRAINNE

One fine morning, Finn Mac Cool rose early and went
out on the dew of the grass. Oisin, his son, and
Dering the druid saw him there in the dawn
and went to speak to him.

'This is early rising, Finn,' said Oisin.

'Not without cause,' said Finn. 'Since my wife died from
me, there is no quiet sleep for me.'

'There is remedy for that,' said Oisin. 'Throw your glance
on the most or least girl in all green Ireland and we will bring
her to you for your wife.'

'I myself know a worthy woman,' said Dering. 'It is
Grainne, the daughter of King Cormac Mac Art. She is the
woman of the best look and shape and speech in all Ireland.'

'There is strife between Cormac and myself,' said Finn. 'It might please him to refuse me in my person. But go the two of you and ask for his daughter, for he may speak better to you than to me.'

Then the two of them went to Tara to see the king, and they asked for his daughter Grainne in marriage for Finn Mac Cool, captain of the Fianna.

'There is not a champion in Ireland,' replied the king, 'who has not been refused by Grainne. But I will take you and you will find the answer from her own mouth.'

Cormac took the messengers to the women's house and sat in the seat beside his daughter.

'Here, Grainne,' he said, 'are two of the people of Finn, who would have you for Finn's wife. What say you?'

'If he is fit to be your son-in-law,' said she, 'then why should he not be my husband?'

They were satisfied with that answer, and a time was appointed in two weeks for Finn to come to Tara. Finn collected seven battalions of the Fianna from every part of Allen in Leinster, and they went bravely in bands and troops into Tara. The wedding feast was prepared in the great hall, and the people of Cormac and the people of Finn were seated in their places.

Then Finn spoke to Grainne and questioned her.

'What is hotter than fire?' he said.

'A woman's reasoning between two men,' she replied.

'What is swifter than the wind?'

'A woman's thought between two men.'

'What is sharper than a sword?'

'The reproach of a foe.'

'What is softer than down?'

'The palm on the cheek.'

'What is whiter than snow?'

'There is truth.'

'What is blacker than the raven?'

'There is death.'

Finn asked no more, for he was satisfied. But Grainne was not satisfied.

Now it chanced, as the feast went on, that Daire the poet was close to Grainne and they passed pleasant talk between them. After a while Grainne said, 'Why have this Finn and his Fianna come here? And what means his questioning of me?'

Daire was mighty surprised at this and replied, 'Do you not know that he comes to take you as wife?'

She was a long time silent. Then she said, 'If Finn wished me for his son Oisin or for his youthful grandson Oscar, it would be no wonder. But I marvel that he wants me for himself. He is older than my father, with many white hairs.'

Then she thought again, and she looked well around the table. 'This is good company,' she said, 'but I know not these men, apart from Oisin, son of Finn.'

So Daire named many heroes, and told her of their strength and boldness and high lineage, till she stopped him at a certain face.

'What is that youth of the sweet words,' she asked, 'with the fair, freckled cheeks and the raven-black curls?'

'That man is Diarmuid, grandson of Duibhne, and he is the best lover of a woman in the whole world.'

'That is good company indeed,' said Grainne.

She called her servant to bring a great golden cup, to fill it to the brim, and to pass it around the table. Finn drank, and Cormac drank, and so the cup went around till all had drunk except Diarmuid. Then Grainne stopped the cup, and soon all who had drunk were in a sleep like the sleep of death. Then Grainne rose softly and went down the hall to sit by Diarmuid.

'Receive my love, Diarmuid,' said she, 'and give me back your own.'

'I will not, and I dare not,' said he, 'meddle with a woman who is promised to Finn Mac Cool.'

'Then, O Diarmuid, I will put you under a *geasa*, a spell of danger and destruction, if you do not take me out from this house tonight, before Finn and the king awake.'

'Those are evil bonds, woman,' replied Diarmuid, 'and why have you chosen me above many great men at this feast? Not one of them is less worthy of love than myself.'

'Do not question me. My eye fell on you, and my love followed my look.'

'But it is a hard burden you place on me. And do you not know that when Finn sleeps at Tara, he himself keeps the keys of the house?'

'All the world knows,' she replied, 'that a good warrior of Ireland can leap the wall by the shafts of his spear. You shall do that, and I shall follow through a little hidden door.'

Then Diarmuid took counsel among his own people. Oisin and Oscar and other companions told him to go with Grainne, for it was a bad stroke indeed to break the bond of a *geasa*, and the maiden herself was worthy to be loved. But Dering the druid spoke a warning.

'In the footsteps of that woman death awaits you. But you must go with her, for the spell and the bond placed upon you shall not be broken.'

When he heard this, Diarmuid made one last appeal.

'My friends, is this your counsel?' he cried.

'Yea, it is so,' they said, one and all.

So Diarmuid armed himself, and he wept some tears for his friends. Then he stood before the wall and thrust down on his spears, and with a light airy leap he cleared the wall of the fort and the ditch beyond. On the green of the field Grainne was waiting, but still Diarmuid held back.

''Tis a bad journey we are starting on,' said he. 'Much better for you would be Finn Mac Cool. Who in all Ireland can hide us from his anger? Return now, before the sleepers awake.'

'I will not go back,' she replied, 'and I will not part from you till death carries me away.'

There was no more to say. Away they went before the dawn, westward into Connacht. They crossed the ford on the Shannon and came to Two-Hut-Wood in Clanrickard. Diarmuid cut branches and made a fence with seven wattle doors, and in the middle he made for Grainne a bed of soft rushes and the tops of the birch-trees.

When Finn saw that the lovers were gone, a burning jealousy seized him. At once, he sent trackers from the Clan

Navin after them, but they lost the scent at the Shannon. Finn was so angry, he was about to hang the sons of Navin without delay. But the trackers, having a good reason for greater effort, went hurriedly up the river-bank and picked up a trail that led to Two-Hut-Wood. Then Finn was sure that he had caught the lovers.

But the friends of Diarmuid wished to warn him of the danger, and Oscar went to one side to give orders to Finn's hound, Bran. Bran pricked his ears and understood well. He ran ahead into the wood and hunted out the hiding-place. Then he thrust his nose into the bosom of sleeping Diarmuid.

Diarmuid started from sleep and said, 'Here is Bran, Finn's hound. Surely this is a warning that Finn is near.'

'Take the warning,' said Grainne, 'and fly.'

'I will not,' replied Diarmuid, 'for Finn is hard to escape. It is best to face him here, where I am prepared.'

When nothing moved in the wood, Oisin feared that Bran had failed, and he looked for another warning. He sent for Fergor, whose shout might be heard in three distant counties, and Fergor sent three roars that Diarmuid could not miss.

'I hear the shouts of Fergor,' said Diarmuid, 'it is certain that Finn is upon us.'

'Take the warning and fly,' said Grainne, but still he would not. Then fear and great dread came on Grainne.

Now the trackers had entered the wood and they searched all about till they came to the strong fence that Diarmuid had made.

'This is the work of Diarmuid,' said Finn, raising his voice. 'Is it not so, O Diarmuid?'

'Your judgment does not err,' came the answer. 'Grainne and I are indeed here.'

Then he comforted Grainne openly with three kisses, which Finn saw, and it made him rage. He put a company of the Fianna to guard each wattle gate so none might escape.

Now, this meeting and challenge in the wood came to the ears of Angus Og in Brugh on the Boyne. He feared that his foster-son Diarmuid was in the greatest danger, so he set out on a clear cold wind and did not rest till he came secretly into Two-Hut-Wood.

'Let each of you come under the border of my cloak,' said he to the lovers, 'and I will fetch you from here without the knowledge of Finn and the Fianna.'

Grainne agreed but Diarmuid would not go. So Angus put her into the shadow of his cloak and away they fled to Two-Willow-Point at Limerick. But Diarmuid stood straight as a pillar and armed himself. He went to the first of the seven gates and called out, 'Who is there?'

'No enemy of yours,' was the answer, 'but only Oisin and Oscar. Come forth to us without harm.'

'I will not,' said Diarmuid, 'for I seek Finn.'

He went from gate to gate, finding friends only, till he came to the gate held by the sons of Navin.

'Come out,' they cried, 'and we will mark you with swords and spears.'

'No fear of you, you sour-faced sniffing dogs, keeps me within,' replied Diarmuid, 'but your blood would be a stink on my weapon.'

He went to the last gate and heard from beyond a loud voice that said, 'Finn Mac Cool and the men of the Fianna are here. No love awaits you. Come without and we will spill the marrow from your bones.'

But Diarmuid rose on the shaft of his spears and jumped high and lightly far over the heads of Finn's people. They did not see him, and in a moment he was on his way to Two-Willow-Point. And there he found Angus Og and Grainne in the snug of a hut, with a fire a-blaze and the half of a wild pig turning on the spit. And when Grainne saw him, the life all but went out of her for joy.

Early next morning Angus rose to leave, but before he went he had advice for his foster-son.

'O Diarmuid,' he said, 'in your flight from Finn go not into a tree with one trunk, nor into a cave with one opening, nor to an island with only one approach. Where you cook, eat not there. Where you eat, sleep not there. Where you rest tonight, sleep not tomorrow night. And so farewell.'

Many times, in the days that followed, the lives of Diarmuid and Grainne were in danger. Finn looked for them far and wide. Enemies from the sea and venomous hounds chased them till at last they left Two-Willow-Point and went into the forest of Dubhros, where there was a famous quicken-tree, or rowan. This rowan grew from a berry brought by the Tuatha De Danann from the Land of Promise. The Tuatha De Danann had dropped the berry by accident during a hurling-game against the Fianna, and from it grew a wonderful tree. The berries of this tree had the taste of honey, and those who ate them felt the liveliness of wine, and a person of a hundred had the youth again of one aged thirty.

The guardian of the tree was a Fomorian from Lochlann called Searbhan the Surly, and he was very big and black and ugly, with crooked teeth and a single eye in the middle of his forehead. He had a belt of iron and a club of iron, and he would not die except from three strokes of his own club. Fire could not burn him, nor water smother him, nor weapons kill him. He slept in the tree by night and watched it by day, and he made a wilderness around where none, not even the men of the Fianna, dared hunt or chase. If Diarmuid and Grainne could settle there, it would be a safe place for them.

Diarmuid went to this giant and made a bond with him to live there and hunt so long as he touched not the rowan or the berries. Diarmuid made a hut and he and Grainne lived safely in the wood of Dubhros, eating beasts from the wild and drinking water from the spring.

Now, Finn at this time had returned to Allen, and there came to him to sue for peace enemies from the past, men of the families that had slain Finn's own father at the battle of Knocka. The leaders on this journey were Angus, son of Art Mac Morna, and Aed, son of Andala.

'Peace you may have,' said Finn, 'but what fine will you pay in satisfaction for my father's death?'

'We have no gold or silver or cattle to give you,' said they.

'Then I shall ask from you one of two things only. The

190

head of a champion, or the full of my fist of the berries of a rowan tree.'

But Oisin warned the two chiefs and said, 'Take counsel, you children of Morna, for it is not an easy thing that Finn asks you. The head he is asking is that of Diarmuid O'Duibhne, and twenty times your number would hardly be enough for that task. As for the berries, they are the magic fruit of the rowan in the wood of Dubhros, which is guarded by Searbhan the Surly.'

'Since peace is our great desire,' replied the chiefs, 'let us pay the fine or die in the attempt.'

Then they went with many arms to the wood of Dubhros and called out for Diarmuid. He met them with weapons in his hands and heard their demands.

'It is a melancholy thing for you,' said Diarmuid, 'to be under bonds to that Finn. Did he not himself slay your own two fathers in revenge for the death of his father, and should not that be satisfaction enough for him?'

'That is not well said,' the chiefs answered. 'First you steal his wife, and then you speak ill of him. It is best if we fight.'

They agreed, for the better display of valour and honour, to fight without weapons, by the strength of their hands only. But the two chiefs were as infants in Diarmuid's grasp, and he threw them down and tied them fast.

Diarmuid and Grainne had a relief from this victory, and Grainne in her happiness found a great wanting for the magic berries of the rowan. She told Diarmuid that she must have them or die. To hear this was no pleasure for Diarmuid as he had made a pact with the surly giant. The two chiefs were listening to Grainne and they said, 'Untie us and we will help you in this task.' Diarmuid doubted this. But as their lives were already forfeit to him, he took them with him for whatever help they might give.

Searbhan the Surly was dozing at the foot of the rowan. Diarmuid gave him a thump with his foot, and the giant raised his baleful red eye.

'Have you a mind to break our peace, grandson of Duibhne?' said he.

'Not so,' said Diarmuid, 'but Grainne has a great desire for those berries, and I would have them for her.'

'Not even to save a child in her womb would I give her those berries.'

'Still, she must have them or die, and I shall fetch them whether you wish it or not.'

Then Diarmuid and the giant fought. Diarmuid cast aside his weapons and moved in close. He grappled the giant by his iron belt and heaved him from his feet. With a nimble skip he caught up the giant's own club and knocked out his brain with three mighty blows. Then, while Diarmuid rested, the two chiefs put the huge body under the sod and went to call Grainne. Diarmuid plucked berries for her, and the sons of Morna filled a fist from the top of the tree to take to Finn. The fruit from the top of the tree was sweetest of all, but the ones from below were bitter.

As the two chiefs returned to Finn they called out. 'We have killed the surly giant, and we bring you the berries of the rowan tree. Let that be for your satisfaction, and now let us go in peace.'

But when they handed the berries to Finn, he put them to his nose.

'These berries,' he said, 'have the smell of Diarmuid on them. He plucked them, not you. And sure I am that he killed the surly giant. I will go now and see for myself.'

Finn summoned the seven battalions of the Fianna and away they all marched to the wood of Dubhros. They saw that the rowan was unguarded and they filled themselves with the berries as much as they pleased. In the hot sun of noon they lay down to rest, while Diarmuid and Grainne were in the nest of the giant at the top of the tree.

In the quiet of this hour Finn set out his chessboard to pass the time, and he played a game against his son Oisin. After a while there was but one move to make to win the game, though Oisin could not see it. But Diarmuid was awake and watching from the top of the tree, and he threw a berry that hit the piece to be moved. Oisin did so, and the game was won. They played again, and so it happened twice more that

Diarmuid threw a berry for the winning move, and the Fianna gave a great shout that the games were won.

'It is a fine thing for you,' said Finn to his son, 'to have in these games the help and advice of Oscar and Dering. But the best of all teaching was that which Diarmuid O'Duibhne gave you.'

'Is it only your jealousy, Finn,' said Oisin, 'to think that Diarmuid would stay in this tree, and you within his reach?'

Then Finn called out in a loud voice, 'Who speaks the truth, myself or Oisin?'

'True for you, Finn,' Diarmuid replied. 'I myself and Grainne are above, in the bed of the surly giant.'

Grainne began to tremble and weep, but Diarmuid comforted her with three kisses, in the sight of Finn and all the Fianna. Then Finn was scorched with anger and jealousy.

'Your head shall be the price, Diarmuid,' he cried, 'for those three kisses.'

The men of the Fianna surrounded the rowan, standing hand in hand, and one after another nine warriors climbed into the tree to bring Diarmuid down. But with kicks and blows Diarmuid hurled each to the ground and killed every one.

While the Fianna were making this attack, Angus Og again heard that his foster-son was in deadly trouble. Quickly he flew through the pure cold air and threw his druid's cloak around Grainne and carried her away to Brugh on the Boyne. When Diarmuid saw her safely gone, he called out to Finn.

'I will come down now,' he cried, 'for I am certain you will give me no rest till you have killed me. Is there no friend or comrade who will welcome me in any part of the great world? Often I fought for the love of you, Finn, and for the sake of the Fianna. Then listen well. You will pay hard for me, and my death will be no free gift.'

When Oscar heard this he was troubled in his heart and he went to his grandfather Finn.

'It is a shame and a reproach on you,' he said to Finn, 'that you will not give peace to our warrior Diarmuid. But I give my word under the heaven that I will not let you or the Fianna of Ireland hurt him. I will shorten the bones of any man who attacks him. Then come you down, Diarmuid, and leave in peace. On my body and life no harm shall touch you today.'

Diarmuid felt joy at these words. From a high bough of the tree he pressed on the shafts of his spears and sailed lightly and airily over the heads of the surrounding Fianna. Oscar met him, and together they retreated, clearing their way with a flight of javelins that sounded like the rush of water in a rocky stream.

Then they were beyond reach, and the Fianna put up their weapons and marched with Finn back to Allen in Leinster.

Sixteen years went by, and then one morning early Angus Og went through the pure cold air to the house of Finn and asked him to make peace with Diarmuid O'Duibhne. Finn was weary of the enmity, with such time lost, and so many killed. He agreed to give up the hunt against Diarmuid and Grainne. King Cormac Mac Art and Diarmuid himself were also glad to make an end of the feud, and thus it was done on the condition that Diarmuid, for his suffering, was given certain good lands.

These lands were granted. Then Diarmuid and Grainne went far away and lived in the place called Rath Grainne in the district of Kesh Corran. Grainne bore five children, four sons and one daughter, and the folk of that country agreed that there was no man more content than Diarmuid, nor any richer in gold and jewels and sheep and cattle-herds.

After many years Grainne's heart began to yearn for her father, for she had had no sight of him from the day they left Tara. She also thought it a poor thing that, rich and settled as they were, they had never welcomed to their house Finn Mac Cool, for Cormac and Finn together were the two best men in all Ireland.

'What are you saying, Grainne?' replied Diarmuid. 'Would you give me to my enemies?'

'What is done is forgotten,' said she, 'and a good feast soothes memories and is a way to the heart.'

So for a full year they were preparing for the visit and the feasting. Then Cormac came, and Finn with the seven battalions of the Fianna, and they all stayed in Rath Grainne for another year of good fellowship.

On the last day of that year Diarmuid was in his sleep when he heard the voices of hounds go through his dreams. He started up, but lay down again in the sweet comfort of Grainne's arms. Three times this happened. Then he rose in the weak dawn light and went out after the baying of the dogs, with his small sword at his side, and his little spear in one hand, and the lead of his hound Mac an Chuill in the other.

Diarmuid went to the top of Ben Bulbin and found Finn there alone. Finn told him that some men of the Fianna had set out at midnight on the scent of a boar. But the trail was lost and it was pointless to continue.

'Many a time,' said Finn, 'we have hunted that boar to no end except danger and damage to us. This very night he has killed thirty of our men. And now let us leave with speed, for I hear him coming up the mountain.'

'I will not leave this hill,' said Diarmuid, 'for fear of a wild pig.'

'You had best do it, Diarmuid, for this is the earless and tailless boar that you are under a *geasa* not to hunt. Angus Og in your young days put you under this bond, for he knew the boar was likely to be the death of you.'

'I know nothing,' replied Diarmuid, 'of the incantations and prophecies of my childhood. But here I stay. Leave me your hound Bran to help my Mac an Chuill, and I will take my chances.'

But Finn and his hound were away down the mountainside, and the boar was showing his fierce snout over the shoulder of the hill. Diarmuid unleashed Mac an Chuill, but the hound took one look and was gone with his tail tucked in behind. Diarmuid put his finger in the silken loop of his little spear and cast it full force into the face of the boar. But it made not so much as a scratch. So he drew his small sword and gave a smart heavy blow, which left the sword in two parts and the boar still unhurt.

'Alas,' cried he, 'Grainne told me this morning to take my large sword and great spear. To spurn the advice of a good woman, that is indeed a foolish thing.'

Then the boar made a charge that cut the sod from below Diarmuid's feet and felled him. The beast wheeled and made another rush, and with his tusk he opened Diarmuid's side from neck to thigh. As he took this wound, Diarmuid got a hold on the boar and drove the jagged broken blade of the sword through the eye-socket and into the brain. The brute fell dead on the spot.

It was not long before Finn and some men of the Fianna came back up the mountain and saw that the bowels of Diarmuid were hanging out of him and death was very close.

'Now it pleases me well,' said Finn to Diarmuid, 'to see you in this way. Only I wish that the women of Ireland might see you also, with your handsome looks befouled and your proud body in a broken heap.'

'Those are ignoble words,' said Diarmuid. 'And it lies within your power to heal me, if you wished.'

'How so?' said Finn.

'When you received the gift of foreknowledge at the Boyne, it was granted to you also that you could heal all those who drank from out of your hand.'

'You are not deserving of this healing power,' replied Finn. 'At Tara, secretly you stole Grainne from me, though you were then under orders to guard her.'

'Blame me not for that, Finn. Grainne put the heavy bonds of a *geasa* upon me, and this I could not break through on my life or all the world. But remember the goodness of all my past service to you and the Fianna. From the day I was first admitted among the Fianna, I did save you in many deadly straits. Always I put myself in the worst place of danger and wagered my body on behalf of your safety. Good men have died for you, and yet there is no end to death. I see a day coming for the overthrow and slaughter of the Fianna, and few of their seed will be left after them. Then

196

you would cry for my help, O Finn. But I grieve not for you, old man. My sorrow is for my dear companions of the Fianna, and for Oscar, and for Oisin who shall be lamenting after the Fianna during many long years.'

Then Oscar turned on Finn in anger and said, 'My blood is nearer to you than to Diarmuid, but your unkindness warrants a strong reply. By the power of my hand, give him a drink without delay!'

Nine paces away there was a well of fresh water. Finn went with slow steps and took water in the full of his two hands. But then he thought of Grainne, and he let the water dribble between his fingers.

'How could you spill it?' groaned Diarmuid. 'O hasten, for my death is near.'

So Finn fetched water and spilt it again. And Diarmuid, when he saw it, gave a piteous wail of anguish.

'I swear,' cried Oscar in his rage, 'if you do not bring water, only one of us will leave this hill alive.'

Then Finn saw the black looks of his men, and he hurried to Diarmuid with water in his hands. But the life had fled from the body, and all the men of the Fianna gave three heavy shouts of sadness and despair.

And after a time Finn sad, 'Let us go softly now, lest Angus Og come upon us. We had no hand in Diarmuid's death, but would Angus believe it?'

Diarmuid's hound had crept back, to whine at the death. Finn took it by the lead and went down the hill. The friends of Diarmuid wrapped him in their cloaks and followed Finn.

As they came towards the fort, Grainne was on the wall, waiting for news. When she saw the hound led in without the master, her spirit fled from her and she pitched forward in a faint. And when she had recovered she sent five hundred of her people to bring Diarmuid from the mountain. The procession approached slowly, and she was keening for her dead lover.

'O Diarmuid,' she cried, 'my handsome man, Finn has given you a hard bed indeed, lying on stones in the wet of the rain. Your blue eyes are closed. You were my hawk and my hound, my secret love hunted with you. And you were the prop for the men of Ireland, the head in every battle. Now I hear your harp no more. I am sorrowful, without mirth, without light. I am grief, I am dying. O Diarmuid, you pitiful man!'

Then as she was crying, suddenly there was another by her side, for Angus Og had flown on the pure cold wind to claim the body of his foster-son.

'The boar of Ben Bulbin has cut you down,' Angus lamented, 'as the prophecy foretold, O my Diarmuid of the bright face. Did I abandon you to the treachery of Finn? Certainly I shall forever feel the bitter pangs of sorrow. Take up the body now and bring it to the Boyne. I cannot restore his life, but I shall breathe a spirit into him so that every day, for a little while, we may talk together as we used to do.'

They took the body and placed it on a golden bier, and over it were the upward-pointing spears of Diarmuid. Then they went on a long road till they came to Brugh on the Boyne.

Finn Mac Cool saw now that Oisin and Oscar and many bold men of the Fianna had abandoned him. He did not know how he could face the danger from them, and the danger from Diarmuid's sons, without the help and forgiveness of Grainne. So he went secretly to Rath Grainne and cunningly gave her sweet words. She reviled him with her keen sharp-pointed tongue. But he flooded her mind with gentle and loving speech till he brought her to his own will. Then he got from her the desire of his heart and soul.

Finn took Grainne by the hand and they went towards the Fianna of Ireland. When the warriors saw them coming together, with the look of a man and his wife, they raised a great shout of mockery and derision, and Grainne bowed her head in shame.

'Now we know, O Finn,' Oisin called out, 'that Grainne will be ever in the sight of your best eye from this time on.'

Some said that the changes in a woman's mind flow like running water, but others said that Finn had put a spell on Grainne. But certain it is that they stayed by one another till the day of death.

6

FINN MAC COOL
AND
THE FENIANS

Hear the words of Finn, and hide them not.
It grieves me to see the number of grey-faced
  foreigners,
Though I myself would be driving them out.
But soon I and the Fianna shall not exist.

Round Sligo a battle will be fought.
It is unlikely that I shall be present,
Much it grieves me, O woman.

First psalmist of the Irish am I,
The Son of God will carry me to heaven.
I dislike the nature of women, but I've had
  many of them.
I am Finn, son of the noble Cool.
I believe in the King of Heavens.
I am the best prophet under the sun,
Though I have done the will of women.

FINN'S BIRTH
AND YOUTH

At the time of the birth of Finn Mac Cool, his father, of the family of Baskin, was killed in the battle of Knocka by the sons of Morna. Then there was danger for the little lad, for the enemies of his family wished to kill him also. They took him from his mother and threw him from the window of the fort into a loch. But the babe rose again holding hard to the tail of a big salmon.

It happened that his grandmother was walking by the shore and saw him come up from the water.

'Is it not my grandson,' she cried, 'the true son of my own true child?' And she caught the babe from the water and vanished away with him to the deep forest.

In the heart of the forest she saw a woodman by a great oak tree, and she asked him to cut a chamber in the tree. He set to and made a nice snug room, big enough for her and the babe and the little whelp-hound she had brought with her. As the axe fell, the fine chippings flew, and the pup ate them up.

'Is it good eating?' the old woman laughed. 'Now you will be called Bran, or the Wood-chip, from this time out.'

Then the work was finished and she asked the woodman for the axe. He gave it into her hand, and in a minute she swept the head off him, saying, 'Your tongue will never tell of this place.'

All three together lived in the tree, and the woman did not take the lad out till he was five years old and still unable to walk. Then she took the boy to the top of a hill and gave him a good cut with a switch.

'Tumble down the hill,' said she, 'and I'll be after you with this switch. But on the way up I'll go ahead and you can strike at me.'

At first, the lad got all the blows. But very soon he was so nimble on his feet that his grandmother could not reach him. But he whipped her uphill with a stroke at every step.

When the youth was fifteen, a great runner and a strong hearty lad, the old woman took him to a hurling match where his enemies were taking part. The young fellow joined the play against his enemies. He took the ball in the air and carried it up and down and drove it through the goal so that he won every game. The old king was angry at the defeat of his people. He cried out against the young skilful runner with the very fair hair, wanting to know who was this youth with the *finn cumhal*, that is to say the 'white cap'.

'Aye, that is it,' said the old woman. 'Finn will be his name, and Finn Mac Cool he is.'

Then the old king knew it was his enemy, and he ordered Finn to be seized and killed on the spot. But the old woman took her grandson by the hand and away they went, a hill at a leap, a glen at a step, and thirty miles at a jump. The pursuers were after them, and they all ran a long while till Finn was tired. Then the grandmother took him on her back, putting his feet into two pockets of her dress, and ran on as swiftly as before.

Still the pursuers were after them, and the hot breath was on their backs.

'Look behind, young Finn,' said the grandmother, 'and tell me what you see.'

'A white horse,' said he, 'with a champion on his back.'

'Nothing to fear,' she replied, 'for a white horse has no endurance. He'll not catch us.'

On they went and the breath of pursuit on their backs was hotter yet.

'I see a warrior on a brown horse,' said Finn.

'Nothing to fear,' said she, 'for a brown horse is giddy and will not overtake us.'

But the next time Finn looked he saw a black warrior on a black horse following fast.

'Now we'll not escape,' said the old woman. 'There's no horse so tough and resolute as a black one. Since one of us must surely die, save yourself.'

Then Finn slipped off her back, and she went headlong into the deep bog and sank to her neck. The black rider galloped to the edge of the bog calling out, 'Where's Finn?'

'Here in the bog before me,' she replied. 'Can you not see I'm trying to find him?'

'One white head,' he said, 'may please the king as well as another.' With that, he cut off her head and rode away.

After this, Finn wandered the land with his hound, Bran. He learnt the two ways of poetry and the three ways of wisdom. He knew the songs for all the seasons, but the long tales of winter pleased him best.

'The ox is lowing in the stall,' he used to sing, 'high and cold is the wind, low the sun, the sea full of quarrelling cries, the summer is gone. The ferns grow red and their shape is hidden. The wild geese cry, cold has caught the wings of the bird. The ice-frost comes. I have another story to tell. Listen.'

When Finn was ready in himself, he went for the feast of Samhain to the court of the high-king at Tara. Now, it was the law of the feast that none should bring there any grudge or quarrel. The high-king was in his place, and with him were Caoilte, son of Ronan, and sharp-tongued Conan, and Goll son of Morna, the chief of the Fianna. The Fenian warriors of the Fianna were ranged all about, and into this company came the young Finn, though none knew who he was.

The high-king saw him and put the drinking-horn of meeting into his hand and asked who he was.

'I am Finn Mac Cool,' said he, 'son of the man who was both king of Ireland and chief over the Fianna. And I am come to get friendship and to give service.'

'Then indeed you are the son of a friend,' replied the high-king, 'and a well-trusted man.'

The high-king took Finn by the hand and between them they made a bond of loyalty and service, and then they all fell to good eating and good drinking.

Now, every year at Samhain-time there came out of the north a man of the Tuatha De Danann and he set fire to Tara. Aillen was his name. The way it was, he came with the music of the *shee* that turned all who heard it towards sleep. While they slept, he let a flame out of his mouth that burned all Tara. The coming of this man was a fear and sorrow for the king.

'He who could stop Aillen,' said he, 'I would give him whatever inheritance he wished, little or much.'

The men of Ireland were silent, for they knew the power of the sweet pitiful music of the *shee*. When it sounded, even wounded men and women in labour fell asleep. But Finn took the task upon himself and promised safety from the fire of Aillen.

It was a hard promise to make good. While Finn was thinking on the matter, there came to him Fiacha, son of Conga, his father's old friend.

'Well, boy,' said he, 'would I bring you a deadly spear that never made a false cast?'

'What would you be asking for it?' said Finn.

'A third of what your right hand wins and a third of your trust and friendship.'

'Willingly, you shall have it,' said Finn.

Fiacha brought him the spear in secret and said, 'When you hear the music of the *shee*, let you pull the cover from the head of the spear and hold it to your forehead. The power of the spear will keep sleep from your eyes.'

Finn rose with the spear and stood guard by the gate at Tara. Soon he heard the approach of the long sorrowful music. He stripped the cover from the head of the spear and put it to his forehead, and then he was awake before the face of Aillen. Fire was belching from the mouth of Aillen but Finn caught the flames in his crimson cloak, and wrapped the fire in his cloak, and buried it deep in the sod of the earth.

When Aillen saw that his spell was broken, he fled back to the north. But Finn chased him hard, and caught him at the very door of his house, and pierced him through and through with a cast of the spear. He cut off his head and took it back to Tara and fixed it on a crooked pole. In the rising dawn the high-king and his chief men and the Fenians saw the gory head of Aillen ringed with sunlight, and they knew that Tara was saved from fire.

Then the chief men of Ireland came together in council, and they agreed that Finn Mac Cool, son of a renowned father, should become leader of the Fianna of Ireland, and all the Fenian should swear loyalty to him.

'Well, Goll,' said the high-king to the son of Morna, 'is it your choice now to quit Ireland, or to give way and put your hand in the hand of Finn?'

'By my word, I will do that,' said Goll. And he was the first to give his hand so that the rest might easily follow.

Now Finn remained captain of the Fianna till the end, and the place where he lived was Allen in Leinster, in the great pale fort made by Nuada of the Tuatha De Danann out of the white lime of Ireland mixed with the white horns and bones of cattle.

As to Finn Mac Cool himself, he was a chief and a poet and a man of wisdom, and all he said was sweet-sounding to his people. And never was there a better fighting man, and whatever anyone said about him he was still three times better than that. Fair justice he gave, even between his enemy and his own son. Generous he was, and never denied any man who had a mouth to eat with, or legs to bring away what was given him. He left no woman without her bride-price, and no follower without pay. He promised at night only as much as he could do on the morrow, and he fulfilled at night what he had promised in the day. Never did he forsake his friend.

But if he was quiet in peace, he was angry in battle. And his son Oisin and his grandson Oscar were at one with him in the madness and raging heart they all showed in the red mist of the battle.

FINN IN THE HOUSE
OF CEANN SLIEVE

At the beginning of summer, Finn Mac Cool feasted the chief people of Ireland at Allen on the broad hill-slopes. And when the feast was done, it was time to start the chase through the wilderness of Ireland.

Now this was the way of it, how the Fenians spent their time. Each year, from May to November, they hunted with their dogs every day. But from November to May they lived in the friendship of the land, so that there was not a chief or a great lord in the whole country who had not nine of the Fenians lodged with him for a half of the year.

At this time, after the feast, Finn and his men went to hunt the stag on the mountain of Torc, by Loch Lein. They had started up the most nimble bucks, scared foxes astray, roused badgers from the clefts, driven birds to the wing. The fawns and young animals had shied away to the very summit.

207

Fenian hands were stained with blood and hounds were mangled with gore, for success was theirs that day.

But Finn had lagged behind and only Dering was with him at the end of the hunt.

'Well, Dering,' said Finn, 'do you take the watch while I sleep, for I rose early this day. And it is early rising when a man cannot see his five fingers against the sky, or tell a hazel from an oak.'

Then Finn fell into a pleasant slumber. At last, Dering had to wake him, for the night was close upon them and they had no safe place for the dark. So Finn rose and they went on till they saw a strong, well-lit fort on the edge of a sheltering wood. They knocked at the gate and told their names.

'May poison and crushing into pulp be your portion,' said the porter. 'Unfortunate is your visit, for the lord here is Conan of Ceann Slieve, and it was Finn Mac Cool that killed his father, mother and four brothers, and also the father and mother of his wife.'

The porter went away grumbling, to tell the master of the visitors.

'There is at our gate,' he told Conan, 'a tall, fair-haired, manly, powerful fellow, of the best shape. He leads a ferocious, small-headed hound, with the eye of a dragon, claws of a wolf and venom of a serpent, and a collar of bright gold about his neck. There's another fellow too, brown-haired, ruddy-faced, white-toothed.'

'By your description I know them,' said Conan. 'It is Finn of the family of Baskin, the Fenian prince, and his hound called Bran. The other man is Dering. Let them enter.'

So they went in, and their arms were received out of their hands, and a feast was made ready for them. By the one shoulder of Conan was his wife, and by the other was his daughter Finndealbh, a maiden like a pearl, with hair of burnished gold, eyes as blue as the cornflower, and lips more red than the berry of the rowan.

They all sat a while, and it was not easy between them. Then Finn spoke.

'O Conan,' he said, 'true it is that your malice towards me

208

is very great. But recall the time that I saved you and your wife from death, and then we put our hands together in a bond of friendship. At that time your wife was carrying a child, and you promised the child to me. If· a boy, he would become a Fenian. If a girl, she would be raised up for me to marry, should that please me. I see now that she does please me, and I am come to claim her.'

'Cease, O Finn,' replied Conan, 'for she is promised to one as good as you. He is Fatha Mac Avric, son of the king of Easroe.'

'Let your glib tongue be ripped out,' cried Dering, 'and a portion of guilty death be doled out to you! Finn is a better man than all the warriors of the Tuatha De Danann rolled into one body.'

'Be silent, Dering,' said Finn. 'We have not come to commit murder but to get a wife, and we shall have her despite all of the Tuatha De Danann.'

'Let us not quarrel, Finn,' said Conan in a soothing voice. 'Let us talk and then I'll put you under the bond of a *geasa* to answer all my questions. Win victory and blessings, O Fenian chief, and tell me first of the character and quality of the Fenian men.'

'That I may do,' said Finn. 'I myself am the best man, and Deara Dubh is the worst, for he never yet spoke a word that was not reproach and provocation. Liagan is the swiftest, and Life the fire-raiser of Allen is the slowest. The longest journey he ever made, in the length of a summer day, took him from the fountain by the gate of Allen to his own bed. Daolgas is the tallest, and Mac Minne the dwarf is the smallest. Sour Conan Mael with the bald head has the worst temper and the meanest disposition, and Diarmuid is the most handsome. But enough of this for the moment, O Conan. If you have musicians let them come forward now, for it is not my habit to pass any one night without music.'

'What music delights you best?' Conan asked.

'I will tell you. Very sweet to me is the sound of the seven battalions of the Fianna gathering on our plain, with the blast of the dry cold wind whistling about them. And sweet to me is the clink of the cups drained to the last drop in the drinking-hall of Allen. Sweet too is the scream of the seagull and the cry of the heron, the roar of the waves at Tralee, the whistling and humming of Mac Lughaid, the voice of the cuckoo in the first month of summer, the grunting of hogs on the plain of Eitne, and the echo of loud laughter in Derry.'

'Not without interest to me is all that you say,' said Conan of Ceann Slieve. 'But tell me further, O Finn, who was the man that had only one leg, one arm, and one eye, yet escaped you by his great swiftness? And what is the meaning of the saying, "As Roc came to the house of Finn?"'

'No secret there,' replied Finn. And so he told Conan how it came about.

Once, when the Fenians were hunting at Tara, they got nothing but a fawn in the chase. Finn divided it and gave a piece to each hunter, and there remained to him only a haunch bone. He was looking at it without pleasure when he saw hop towards him a huge, black, detestable giant with one eye, one arm, and one leg.

'The talk of men is that you are liberal in gift-giving, O Finn,' said the giant. 'So I have come, by the agility of my arm and leg, to ask for wealth and valuable presents.'

'If I owned all the world,' replied Finn, 'I would give you neither little nor much.'

'Well, then,' said the giant, 'give me at least that haunch in your hand, and allow me the length of a hop to get clear from you, and I'll shake your unfriendly Fenian dust from my shoe.'

So the giant snatched the haunch and hopped over the high stockade of the fort, and he made use of the utmost swiftness of his one leg to outrun all the Fenians except Finn, who went with his minstrels to the top of the fort to watch.

When he saw that the giant was outstripping all others, Finn put on his clothes for running, and taking his sword Mac an Loin in hand he gave chase. He overtook the hindmost at Sliabh an Righ, the middle runners at Limerick, the Fenian chiefs at Athlone, and the swiftest pursuers on the right hand of Cruachan in Connacht, where the giant was less than a stone-shot in front.

The giant hopped the river at Ballyshannon, and Finn leaped after him. Then their course was towards Ben Edar, by a right-hand circuit of Ireland. At the estuary of Howth they both rose over the water, and their leaps were like the flight of birds over the sea. In that great jump, Finn caught the giant by the shirt in the small of his back and laid him to earth.

'You deal unjustly with me, O Finn,' cried the giant. 'My contest was with your Fenians, not you.'

'The Fenians are not perfect,' replied Finn, 'unless I myself am with them.'

Very soon, all the Fenians rushed up, led by Liagan the swift and Caoilte the slender, and they wished to slaughter the giant for his insulting ways but Finn prevented it. So they bound the giant strongly and took him to the house of Bran Beag, where a feast was ready for the Fenians. The giant was thrown to the middle of the hall, and then he spoke.

'Roc, son of Diocan, is my name,' said he, 'and I am foster-son to Angus the Lawgiver of Brugh on the Boyne. My wife poured a current of surprising affection and a deep torrent of love upon Sgiath Breac, who is your foster-son, O Finn. It hurt me hard to hear her boast of the power and swiftness of her lover, and of Fenians in general, and I resolved to challenge in a race all the Fenians of Ireland. But she sneered at me. So my beloved guardian Angus charged me thus, and gave me the swiftness of a druidical wind, as you have seen. That is my history, and you ought to be satisfied with the shame and injury put on me already.'

With this, the giant was set free, and no man knew where he hopped. But that was the cause of the saying, 'As Roc came to the house of Finn.'

'With clear memory and sweet words you relate these things,' said Conan of Ceann Slieve, 'but another thing I would know. What is the meaning of the saying, "The hospitality of Finn in the house of Cuanna?"'

'There is a true tale concerning that,' replied Finn.

On a time when the Fenians were hunting by the summit of Cairn Feargall, they saw a tall, rough, uncouth giant carrying a grunting hog in the prongs of a fork. A well-grown girl followed, driving the giant before her. The Fenians set out fast after the two of them, but a dark, gloomy, druidical mist came down between them.

When the mist cleared they saw a comfortable house at the edge of a ford. There was grass in front of the house, and two fountains. Beside one of these was an iron vessel and beside the other a bronze vessel. About the house were several people. A grey-haired man stood by the door jamb, and a beautiful maid sat before him. The rude, huge giant was cooking the hog on an open fire. Beyond the flames sat an old man with white in his hair and twelve eyes in his head, each beaming with discord. In the house was a ram with white belly, black head, green horns and green feet. And in the end of the house was a hag in a long ash-coloured garment.

'Let homage be done to Finn Mac Cool and his people,' called the man at the door-post. And all the company rose up respectfully.

Finn was thirsty from the hunt and the chase, and when the man saw this he reproached Caoilte, saying, 'To fetch a drink for Finn you have only to step beyond, to whichever fountain you please.'

Caoilte did so and handed Finn a drink. The water tasted like honey as he drank, but like bitter gall when he put the cup down. Darting pains and whispers of death seized him, and agonizing sweats from the poisonous draught. Then the man ordered Caoilte to fetch water from the other fountain. At the first sip of this, Finn never knew such misery, even in the hardship of battle. But when he had finished the drink, health and joy came back to him, to the great happiness of his people.

Then the grey-haired man ordered the giant to divide the hog that was cooking, and he did so evenly among the Fenians and among the folk of the house. But the ram complained that he had been forgotten entirely, and he snatched the quarter given to the Fenians. The ram backed into a corner of the house and began to devour the meat, and then the four Fenians attacked the ram instantly with their swords. But they might as well have laid blows on a rock.

212

'Upon my truth,' said the man with the twelve eyes, 'he is doomed for evil who has companions such as you four fellows, who allow a single sheep to take and eat your portion before your very faces.'

Then he rushed at the sheep, caught him by the feet, and gave him a violent heave out of the door. The ram was seen no more.

When she had eaten, the hag in the end of the house gave a loud belch of wind and suddenly threw her ashy-grey covering over the four Fenians, changing them into four withered, droop-headed old men. Finn himself was seized by fear, but the man by the door-post beckoned him, placed Finn's head on his bosom, and put a great sleep upon him. When Finn awoke, the covering was off his men and they were themselves again.

'O Finn,' said the man of the door-post, 'is it a surprise to you, the happening in this house?'

'Truly, I never saw the like,' said Finn.

'Then I shall tell you what it is. The giant with the hog on the prongs of his fork is he who is yonder, and his name is Sloth. The young woman who was forcing him along, who sits by me here, she is Energy, who whips Sloth to work. The man with many bright eyes is the World, who is more powerful than anyone, as he proved by throwing the ram. The ram is the Crimes of Man. And that hag there beyond, she is wizened Age, and she can afflict even your young Fenian men. The two wells from which you drank are Falsehood and Truth. For a lie is sweet first but bitter last, and the truth is the other way round.

'Cuanna of Innistuil is my own name. I have shown you these thing, O Finn, out of my love for you, and in admiration for your wisdom. Now let you and your men come together, and do you all sleep soft till five in the morning. This story you will not forget, and to the end of the world it shall be called "The hospitality of Cuanna's house to Finn."'

'Good for the telling, O Fenian chief,' said Conan of Ceann Slieve, 'but I have another cause of puzzlement. What reason

was there for your greyness, for the blemish on your coun-
tenance, for the lifeless chill on your skin, for the weakness of
death upon your frame? And how long were you in that
state?'

'These thing are not hidden,' said Finn.

One day, when Finn was having pleasurable drinking in the
hall of Allen of Leinster, and the other chief Fenians were with
him, there came two women of the Tuatha De Danann to offer
him their joint love. They were sisters, Milucra and Aine,
daughters of Cooley.

Aine had boasted that her own husband should never grow
grey, but Milucra summoned the men of the Tuatha De
Danann and had them dig a druidical lake on the slope of
Slieve Cullinn. Any man in the world who bathed in that lake
would become grey and hoary.

Then Milucra took the shape of a fawn upon the plain of
Allen when Finn was hunting alone with his hounds. He
slipped the hounds after the fawn and pursued her to Slieve
Cullinn in Ulster, in the district of Cooley. Hunter and hounds
were close behind, but the fawn reached the mountain
and doubled back and lost the dogs. Finn was exceedingly
astonished that any deer could hold off his hounds in a chase
of such length.

He was puzzling over this when he saw a fair, lovely girl
sitting downcast by the edge of the lake.

'What is the cause of your sorrow, fair maid?' said Finn.

'A ring of red gold have I dropped while bathing,' said she,
'and I now put you under the bond of a *geasa*, O Finn, to bring
it back to me.'

Swimming was not Finn's desire that day, but he would not
suffer himself to be long under a *geasa*. So he dived into the
lake, found the ring and brought it to the girl. With a nimble
leap she sprang over his head into the lake, and then she was
gone.

Finn had left his clothes only a short distance up the shore,
but he had hard trouble to reach them. For he had dived into
the lake of Milucra, and he was changed into a wizened,
decrepit old man. His hounds sniffed at him, but they knew

him not and ran from him. Finn felt so old and weary he could hardly move, so he sat on the edge of the shore till his Fenians arrived, drawn to that place as they followed the noise of the hunt.

'Inform us, old man,' said Caoilte, who was in the lead, 'if you have seen a fawn pursued by two hounds and a man of huge frame and bold, warlike appearance.'

'I have seen them,' replied Finn in a thin, cracked voice, 'and it is not long since they left me.'

He dared not tell the Fenians who he was for his condition was shameful. But he could not keep the secret for long and soon admitted it when all his men were around him. Then they gave three loud cries of surprise and alarm, and ever since that time the lake has been called Loch Doghra.

They made a little cart for Finn and carried him to the *shee* on the hillside that belonged to Cullinn of Cooley. Then the seven battalions of the Fianna spread around the *shee*-mound and dug it away for three nights and days. At the end of that time Cullinn of Cooley came out from the ground and handed Finn a drink in a golden cup. As soon as he drank Finn became himself again, and his strange appearance departed entirely, except for one half of his hair which kept a silvery grey colour. This hoary look in his hair pleased both Finn and the Fenians.

When Finn had drunk, the cup was passed to Mac Reith and then to Dering, and they too drank from it. But as Dering passed the cup, it fell from his hand into the loose earth of his digging. Though every Fenian hastened to save it, it sank before all eyes. This was a cause of affliction to Finn and his people, for had all of them drunk from that cup they would have possessed foreknowledge and true wisdom.

'And that, O Conan,' said Finn, 'is the manner in which I gained both my grey hairs and my true wisdom.'

FINN AND
THE GILLA DEACAIR

A t this time, Finn and his men were hunting towards Knockainy in Munster. The hounds roused up some deer, and then the chase was on, from Ardpatrick to Fermoy, from Hy Conall Gavra across the shores of Loch Lein to the blue stream of Suir. And there was not a plain or a valley or a wood or a brake or a mount or a wilderness in the two provinces of Munster that they did not hunt over.

They reached the plain of Cliach, and here Finn pitched his tent, and he had with him his chief men. Oisin and Oscar, son and grandson, were there, and so was mighty Goll Mac Morna, and that slender man Caoilte Mac Ronan, and Diarmuid O'Duibhne of the bright face, and swift-footed Liagan, and Conan Mael, he of the bald head and the foul mouth.

When all were settled, the deep-voiced hounds were unleashed, and the cry of the dogs as they flushed deer from covers and badgers from dens, to the whoop and whistle of huntsmen and heroes over the broad plain, was sweet music to Finn's ear. Then, when the day's hunt was done, Finn and his men had the chessboard between them, while Mac Bresal stood guard, with a view to the four points of the sky.

He had not been watching long when he saw a Fomorian of vast size leading a horse from the east. It was a great, strong, ugly, clumsy, crooked, flat-footed fellow, with a thin neck, and thick lips, and broken teeth, and hair on his face like an unkempt bush. He was fully armed, but his weapons were old and rusty and dented. He dragged a great iron club that left a furrow as deep as a farmer's plough. The horse he led was as bad as the big lump of the master himself: a large, tangled, scraggy, sooty-black carcass of a beast, with ribs out of his side, and knotty legs, and a twisted neck, and a jaw as long as a jetty.

The great fellow hauled this ugly brute along by a halter, giving the lazy-bones severe blows from his club that sounded like the thunder of surf on the rocks. Mac Bresal was not an easy man to frighten, but now he took his heels from the ground and ran swiftly to Finn's camp. Then with wonder on their faces, all the Fenians watched the coming of this Fomorian.

Slow, heavy steps brought the woeful fellow to Finn, who received a respectful salute. And then Finn had many questions to ask him, as to his birth and lineage, and his craft and his calling, and as to the nature of that ugly brute that could hardly be called a horse.

'O great chief of the Fianna,' was the mournful reply, 'my parents, either noble or ignoble, I did not know. I am a Fomorian of Lochlann in the north. But I dwell nowhere, being a wandering man, looking always for service. You I have heard of, O king, and from you I would now take my wages, which I shall fix myself according to my custom. My name is the Gilla Deacair, or the Slothful Fellow, and for a good reason. There never was a lazier or worse servant than

I, or one that grumbles more. Certainly, I'm a hard fellow to deal with. However noble my master, or however kindly he treats me, he'll get nothing but bad words and foul reproaches from me.'

'It is a poor account indeed you give of yourself,' said Finn, 'and true it is that there's not much to praise in your looks. But I never refused any man service or wages, and I will not refuse you now.'

So they made a covenant and the Gilla Deacair was engaged for a year. Then the Gilla asked Conan Mael whether the foot-men or the horse-men had the better wages among the Fenians. And Conan told him that mounted men had twice as much as the others.

'Horse-service is the one for me,' said the Gilla Deacair, 'as I have a fine horse of my own. And as to this horse, I must attend him myself, for I see no one here worthy to put a hand on him.'

At this, all the Fenians could not help but laugh, for they had never seen such a worthless skeleton of a nag.

The Gilla took his sorry beast to the herd and set him to graze. At once, the horse began to make mischief among the Fenian herd, throwing his tail out as straight as a rod, and thrashing with wild hooves. Left and right, he kicked and butted so that hardly a horse escaped without a broken leg, or a rib fractured, or an eye gouged, or an ear bitten off. Conan roared out to take the monster away, or he himself would knock the brains from the vicious brute. So the Gilla Deacair handed the halter to Conan and told him to try what he would.

In a mighty rage Conan threw the halter over the head of the great bag-of-bones. But the horse stood rigid, as stiff as a log in a little breeze, and try as he might Conan could not shift him an inch. Conan was blue between effort and anger, but the rest of the Fenians were weeping tears of laughter.

'I never thought to see,' said Fergus the poet, 'Conan Mael do such low horse-service. Since you've made yourself a groom to this four-legged devil, would it not be better to get up on his back and revenge yourself for this trouble? A few fierce cuts would drive him up mountains and down valleys. Put him through stones and bogs and crooked places till you've broken the heart in that comical body.'

Stung by taunts and laughs, Conan climbed up on the back of the horse and beat mightily with heels and two heavy fists. But the horse never stirred.

'The reason he will not go,' said Fergus, 'it is that he is used to far more weight. The Gilla Deacair is a heavy lump indeed. Let your friends join you on that uncomfortable height.'

So Conan called for men to join him, and one by one they mounted above till there were, as well as Conan himself, fourteen of the men of Baskin and of the men of Morna on the horse's long back. They all began to thrash with might and main, but never a twitch or a jump did they get out of the beast. And soon they found that their seat was not at all easy, for the back was as sharp and bony as a thin mountain ridge.

When the Gilla Deacair saw the many blows fall on his horse, he was angry and turned against Finn.

'O king,' said he, 'is this true conduct among such famous warriors? Then my service is at an end, and I swear I'll not even wait till morning for my wages. Now I know what to think of Finn and his Fenians.'

With that, he stood straight as a pillar, faced southwest and walked slowly away, with his horse drooping along behind. It was a sight that raised a large hoot of laughter. When he heard this, the Gilla looked back. Then he tucked up his shirt and picked up his heels and ran with such a speed in his long legs that a swallow on a windy March day might hardly keep with him. And his horse, not to be left behind, galloped after him.

Now the men on the back were frightened by the mad bounding of the horse, and they wished to throw themselves off. But the pace was so fast, and the far-away ground looked very hard, and the hooves of the beast whirled most danger-ously, so they clung on for their lives, and Finn and the rest of the Fenians ran after them.

From Cliach plain they flew to Hy Conall Gavra, from

there to Slieve Lougher, from there by Slieve Mish to the deep green sea at Cloghan. Finn and his men were just able to keep the horse in view, but only swift Liagan was fast enough to catch him. At the water's edge he caught hold of the tail with the two of his hands. But the horse still plunged straight into the waves. Liagan was streaming out behind like a banner and the other Fenian riders were clinging hard, their knees clamped fast to the bony ribs and their arms about each other's necks.

Into the wild sea went the horse as easily as upon the dry strand. And though the wave tumbled all around, neither horse nor riders felt a drop of brine or a dash of spray.

Finn and his men stopped at the beach, puzzled by the watery departure of the Gilla Deacair and his horse. Then they saw two young men approaching, in scarlet cloaks held by brooches of gold. It was the two princes, Feradach and Foltlebar, sons of the king of Innia, and they were looking for a chance to practise their arts.

'My art,' said Feradach, 'is the making of a ship without delay. Cover your heads close while I give three blows of my axe and three throws of my sling, and when you open your eyes you shall see a ship all ready.'

'And my art, O chief of the Fenians,' said Foltlebar, 'is the tracking of the wild duck over nine ridges and nine glens, even to the furthest nest. And I can track by sea as easily as by land.'

It was what Finn wished for most, and at once he bound the young men to him. Hardly a moment later there was a ship all prepared, with a guide in the bow. Then some that were steadiest and bravest stayed to guard the kingdom, and Oisin was to be their chief. And others who were bold and adventurous went with Finn in the ship.

Sad was the parting of Finn from his son as he set course towards unknown seas. Foltlebar was guide and navigator, and Feradach the helmsman. The ship was on the broad back of the sea, and soon the high black waves of a great storm came against them. But in the roar of the rain and the blinding spray, Foltlebar still found the track of the Gilla, and Feradach held the helm steady.

As the blackness of the storm cleared, they saw a little way off a towering cliff with its head lost in cloud. It looked as smooth as glass. Examining the four points of the sky, Foltlebar tracked the Gilla and the horse to the foot of the cliff and no further. It was upwards that they must have gone. Then the Fenians were puzzled what to do. They looked at the high smooth rock with vexation in their hearts.

Then the sons of Innia considered the way it was, and Foltlebar thought there might be a way at the backside of the cliff. The Gilla Deacair had taken pains to cover his track, but Foltlebar was the man to sniff it out.

From the backside of the cliff they were off again, by islands and bays and many shores till they reached the Land of Promise. And when they knew where they had come, they were glad of it, for in this land Diarmuid O'Duibhne had been raised by Manannan Mac Lir, the yellow-haired god of the sea.

Now, it was a man of the Tuatha De Danann, named Avarta, who was king here, and this very man had himself taken the form of the Gilla Deacair, to bring the Fenians on the back of the horse into bondage and so to test the power of Finn and the Fianna of Ireland. And when Finn knew that his companions were taken in this country, he planned a speedy onslaught with swords and spears, to make the people learn that none could do outrage to the men of the Fianna and go unpunished.

'It is wise, O Finn, to tread carefully,' said Diarmuid. 'The men here are masters of the druidical knowledge, and it is not safe to stir them up. Let us rather send a messenger to King Avarta, and if he does not free our friends only then will we waste the land with fire and sword.'

Then Foltlebar, the guide, took the messenger by the hand through dim and shadowy places, along paths made crooked by enchantment, till they came to the house of Avarta. The lost men of the Fenians were lying quietly in the sun, not without contentment, for any hard ground was soft enough after a ride on the back of the Gilla's horse.

Then there were tears and many greetings, when the

Fenians saw the messenger. And Avarta himself listened with respect to the message from Finn, for he saw now that Finn had the power and the courage to make good the capture of his men. In a little while Avarta went to meet Finn and he promised the release of the Fenians and a reward for the injury done to them. Then Finn and Avarta joined hands in friendship.

Out of joy to see his Fenian again, Finn wished to lay no fine or penalty on Avarta. But foul-mouthed Conan Mael was not so kind.

'Listen, O Finn,' he said, 'it is an easy matter for you. You have suffered nothing but a little bit of a chase. But we who have endured the sharp bones of the Gilla's horse, the pain of the mad gallop across seas and rocks and deserts and tangled woods, we need some reward for our suffering.'

Those who recalled the sight of the brave Fenian lads helpless on the monstrous horse could hardly keep from laughing. But Avarta did not smile.

'Name your price,' he said, 'and I will pay it all. For I know well your reputation, Conan. I dread the gibes and taunts and insults of your foul tongue.'

'Then let it be done,' replied Conan, 'to you and your people as it was done to us. Let fifteen of the best men of the Land of Promise ride on that long ruinous back, following the very course that we took through thorny forest and jagged rocks and dark glens and storm-bound seas. And Avarta, you yourself shall take hold of the tail of the horse, stuck fast, like a burr on the coat of a wild dog.'

Finn was content that Conan's evil temper had asked no more than like for like, and Avarta was content to make this pledge. Then Finn and his men took their leave, and slid over the broad green sea to Ireland.

They landed and went to their tents at Knockainy and waited for the coming of the Gilla's horse. And sure enough, from the beach at Cloghan the beast came bumping and bucking. Avarta had gone from the back end of the horse to the front. Once more he had taken on the form of the Gilla Deacair, and he was loping along as large and ugly and doleful as before, with the fifteen chiefs from the Land of Promise painfully bobbing behind, like seed-husks in a fast rocky stream.

When the Gilla Deacair and his horse came up to Finn, the Gilla made a wave of his hand towards the clouds and the green hills and the herds of the Fenians peacefully grazing. All the Fenians looked around the familiar land, and it seemed to them that it was good. But when they turned again to the Gilla Deacair, he and his horse and the fifteen chiefs from the Land of Promise had all disappeared, and they were never seen again from that time out.

FINN AND BRAN

One day, Finn was in the front of his house, with no one about him but his hound Bran, when he saw a boat coming to the shore. Three big men jumped from the boat, hauled it seven fathoms length on the green grass, and turned it over so none might launch it. Then they straightened their backs, and one of them looked down towards Finn.

'Well, little fellow,' said he, 'what news can we expect from such a small herd-boy and his wee doggie?'

'No news,' said Finn, 'unless I hear something from big men who have just come from the sea.'

'Our news is that we come to make war and combat with Finn Mac Cool, so go you nimbly and fetch him down.'

Finn went off muttering to himself that he would lay the big men under spells. And he swore by the power of druidical women and the magic of hornless calves to take their heads should he return and find the big men still there.

224

In anger he set sail for the Kingdom of the Big Men, taking only Bran with him. Wind and tide served him well and soon he landed. He looked about him and saw a very tall man going round a tree.

'A grand day,' said Finn.

'Certainly,' said the tall man, 'but what news has the dwarf with the lap-dog?'

'No news,' said Finn, 'but I expect to hear something from a big man going round a tree.'

'The thing I have to tell is this,' replied the tall man. 'Long since has the king of this land wanted a dwarf and a pretty little dog, and now I can bring them to him.'

Away he went, dragging the tree for firewood, and he took Finn and Bran with him. They had not gone far when they met another big man, and he too thought that the dwarf and the pretty dog would be a fine present for the king. So the big men began to fight, till they grew tired.

After a time one of them said, 'Hold your hand now. There's little sense in the work we are doing. Is it not better to lay our quarrel before the dwarf himself?'

'For better or worse,' said Finn, 'I will follow the big man who saw me first.' Then that man lifted Finn in one palm and Bran in the other and went to the house of the king.

The king was well pleased, and he accepted the gift for a year and a day. He gave Finn a chamber next to his own, and Finn was in and out as he wished, ever at the king's side. And he soon noticed that the king was missing every night but returned, cold and wet, just before the dawn. Finn asked the king why this was.

'Should I tell that to the like of you?' said the king.

'There would be no harm to tell it,' replied Finn.

'Not tonight,' said the king, 'so go you to sleep.'

After the next night, when the king was again absent, Finn spoke to him once more.

'A master should tell his mind,' said Finn. 'Let me know the reason for your night departure, or I will not stay with you.'

'What good can it do me,' replied the king, 'to tell such a small weak fellow?'

'Advice may be equally good, from a small man or a tall man.'

So the king said, 'I am seventeen years without sleep or rest, because of a huge monster that worries my kingdom every night.'

'Then sleep tonight,' said Finn, 'and I will meet it.'

'I have need of that sleep,' said the king. But he feared Finn would be destroyed, such a little man was he.

Finn took Bran to the shore. And soon there was a seething-white, rolling, loud-roaring swell out of the sea, and a sea-monster with one blubbery eye measured its great length on the beach.

'Ho,' it said, 'a little man and a smaller dog! What news?'

'The king is dead,' replied Finn. 'Stay away this night, till the nobles get another king to give you combat.'

'Would that be the truth?' said the monster.

'I have no wish to lie,' said Finn. So the monster departed.

When the king awoke from unusual sleep, he cried out in great fear, for he thought that his kingdom was gone together with his dwarf and his lap-dog. But Finn soothed and comforted him.

Next night, the king wished to go to the shore, but Finn and Bran went again in his place. The monster burst from the sea, as before. This time Finn told it that the queen was dead, and once more the kingdom was relieved. Still, the king was full of fear and asked Finn how the monster looked.

'It was not frightening to me,' said Finn.

The king sighed and said, 'You have done much good to give me this rest.'

That night, again the monster came roaring from the sea, shaking its whole blubbery length.

'What news tonight,' it said, 'from the little man and the smaller dog?'

'The news I have is this,' replied Finn. 'It is absurd for such a great brute as you to be listening night after night to lies from such a little fellow as I am.'

'Is that how it is?' the monster shouted. 'Then look to defend yourself.'

It leapt towards Finn and put him to such dodging and twisting that he was soon well-nigh worn out.

'O Bran,' he called to his hound, 'are you likely to remember me at all tonight?'

So Bran took a turn around them and sat where he was before. The wrestling was becoming the worse for Finn, and he called again to Bran, 'Are you like to forget me altogether?'

Bran took a second turn about them and sat down as before. The struggle was now going entirely against Finn, and he was growing faint.

'Bran,' he gasped, 'you need not rise anymore. I am gone. There is no help. What you have done for me, you will never do again.'

Then Bran jumped up and went behind the monster. He uncovered his venomous claw and slashed the monster, and in the blink of an eye the heart and the liver were out of it. Finn hacked off the head, and he rolled it and carried it the way to the king's house. He stuck it on a pole towards the house, with the big goggle eye staring at the king's window. Then he went softly to his place at the feet of the king.

About midnight, the king woke in fear and cried out, 'My kingdom is lost to me, my dwarf and lap-dog are gone.'

'Neither of them is wanting to you,' replied Finn. 'Look from your window and see for yourself.'

The king did so. And when he saw the head and the goggle eye of the monster his knees knocked and he fell beside the bed where Finn lay.

'It was foretold long since,' he said, 'that only Finn Mac Cool would give rest to me and my kingdom. Welcome to you, O Finn Mac Cool!'

'But are you deserving of forgiveness from me?' said Finn sternly. 'Did you not send three big men, without provocation, to combat me in my own kingdom?'

'These are three men,' replied the king, 'who are not under

the law. They are not friendly to me, and their witch-women have made them magic shirts. But when these shirts are taken off them, they will be as other men. I will give you a drink to make them sleep, and then you may strip the shirts from their backs.'

Finn took the drink with him and launched his boat at once, and Bran returned in the boat also. As they came to the shore of his own land, Finn threw out the bottles of the sleeping-draught towards the big men, who were still camped about the house waiting for Finn. The first big man knocked the top off the bottle and drank from it. His companions did likewise, and soon they were all asleep. Then Finn pulled off their shirts and shook them awake.

'Here you are,' said Finn.

'We are,' said they.

'And now you are but as other men, and I have power and chance to take your lives. I shall not release you till you come under a bond of law.'

So they submitted to be bound under covenant. And they swore on the cold sword to stand by Finn in right or wrong, for Finn saw that big men were good men in battle or war. In any danger of distress he had only to think on them and they would be with him wherever he was. Then he restored to them their shirts.

That was satisfactory, and Finn went home to an entertainment that was the fourth greatest ever held among the Fenians.

FINN IN THE HOUSE OF
THE YELLOW-FIELD

This day, Finn and his men were on the hunting hill, and they had done a great deal of chasing before the end of the day, and they had killed a good number of deer.

While they were resting from the hunt, Finn had a look down the glen and saw the appearance of a strong warrior approaching.

'Looks like a stranger is among us,' said Finn.

'If he is coming without business,' said Conan of the foul tongue, 'he will not leave without it.'

After the greeting of the day, the stranger said he was a servant seeking a master, and then Finn was willing to engage him, as was his custom.

'It would not be my advice,' said Conan. 'We have enough of these wandering rogues already.'

'Be quiet, you rascal,' replied the strong lad. 'Your tongue puts your head in trouble, and if I am not deceived you shall indeed suffer some pains on account of the talk this day.'

But Finn smoothed over that talk and asked the lad what wage he wished at the end of a year and a day.

'It is this,' said the lad, 'that you and your men shall go with me to a feast and an entertainment when my time is out.'

All the Fenians took courage from this, that no evil thing should befall them all together. And so the agreement was made.

When his time was out, away went the lad, and it was a hard matter for the Fenians to keep up to him, even for Liagan the swift or slender Caoilte. The big lad set off bare-headed, bare-footed, with a spring from gap to height, from height to glen, through glen to broad valley. With flying foot he led the Fenians till he reached the Yellow-field. When the last breathless man of them had come up to him, he took his way over to a large house and asked them to go in.

Finn entered first, and his men followed. They all got seats by the wall except Conan, who was so far behind he had no choice but to drop down on the hearthstone. At first they were tired and glad for the rest. But soon they grew impatient for the promised feast. After a long time, some of the Fenians offered to go for the food. They tried to rise but they could not. Their haunches stuck to their seats, and the soles of their feet to the floor, and their backs to the walls.

'Did I not tell you in good time,' cried Conan from the hearthstone, 'what would happen with these wandering lads?'

Finn spake not a word, but he was in great anxiety lest this might be the death-strait for all of them. Then he remembered his tooth of knowledge, and he put his finger under it to learn what to do. And it became known to him that nothing would set them free but the blood of the three sons of the King of Inish Tilly, filtered through silver rings into golden cups.

Then he blew his wooden whistle, which he never sounded except in terror of a death-strait. Oscar and Leary had been absent from the company of the Fenians that day, but they heard the whistle. They would have heard it even in the Uttermost World, for the sound passed through the seven borders of the earth.

Three times the whistle sounded, and before the rising of the sun Oscar and Leary were outside the wall of the house in the Yellow-field.

'Are you there within, O Grandfather Finn?' cried Oscar.

'We are within,' Finn shouted back, 'and at our peril.' And then he told them of the blood needed to release them.

'But where shall we watch,' asked Oscar, 'to find the sons of the King of Inish Tilly?'

'Watch well the ford at the mouth of the river over yonder,' said Finn. 'But the day is young yet. See first if you can seek out food for us, for we are faint of hunger.'

Oscar and Leary set their faces towards another big house that was over against them. They found that the cooks were making ready the dinner. As Oscar peeped into the kitchen, he saw a fierce cook lifting a quarter of a deer from the cauldron. In a while the cook departed and Oscar and Leary crept in to steal the food. A buzzard was guarding the pot but Oscar pierced it with a dart, and they ran from the kitchen with every bit of food they could hold.

At the prison-house of the Fenians, Oscar and Leary made a hole in the wall and threw in enough food to satisfy each man, except Conan. He lay on his back, with hands and feet stuck fast to the hearth. Only food dropped from above could get to his mouth. A few pieces and crumbs thrown in the air landed about his face, and in this way he got a morsel or two.

'Now take your watch by the ford at the river mouth,' Finn called, 'for the host from Inish Tilly will be coming.'

'But how shall we know the sons of the king?' said Oscar.

'They will be walking apart on the right hand, and their dress will be all in green.'

Oscar and Leary went to the river mouth and waited at the ford. Soon a great host came in sight.

'Who are those two uncomely lubbers,' shouted the advance guard of the host, 'there at the ford at the beginning of night? It is a time for them to be getting afraid.'

'A third of the fear will be on yourselves,' replied Oscar, 'and only a small bit of it on us.'

'Then wait,' cried the men, 'and it will be to your hurt.'

So they went at each other. Oscar and Leary violently assailed under and over the enemy till not a man of them was left alive to tell the tale. But the sons of the king had not been there that night, and Finn heard this news with sorrow.

'It is needful to try again,' said he. 'But feed us first and watch the ford next. And do not forget to take your three-edged blade and your shield.'

Again the Fenians were fed, though Conan's portion was very small. But still, in the evening, the sons of the King of Inish Tilly did not come to the ford.

'No help but to feed us and prepare again,' said Finn. 'But, Oscar, be sure to carry your spear and shield. If your spear shall taste the blood of the Winged Dragon of Sheil, then the King of Inish Tilly will surely lose a son tonight.'

Now, when Oscar went to steal the food that day, he went armed, and it was well that he did so. The fierce Winged Dragon of Sheil was coiled about the cooking-pot to guard the food. Oscar lifted his shield and with one thrust of his spear he pierced the head of the dragon. As the blood flowed from the dragon the thrashing of its body grew weak, and then it disappeared.

'Did your spear taste blood?' Finn asked when Oscar brought the food.

'A cubit length,' said Oscar, 'and a handbreadth of it drank greedily.'

'Then let your rings for filtering and your cups for holding be with you this night.'

At the ford of the river mouth that evening they saw a host advance with three young men at the right hand in garments of green. Leary stood to face these sons of the king, while Oscar set himself against the rest of the host.

232

'Who are those lubberly fellows at the ford in the evening?' the enemy called out. 'It is time for them to be fleeing.'

'Three-thirds of the fear will be on you now,' replied Oscar, 'for none at all is on us.'

Then Oscar went among that host and cut them about till not one was left alive. And Leary had the three sons of the king on two knees, and they had Leary only on one knee. Leary needed no help, so Oscar put his mind to the blood that was flowing fast onto the ground. He began to filter it through rings of silver into cups of gold, but before the cups were full the bodies were stiff and bled no more.

'Have you the blood?' Finn called out when they returned. 'Then rub it into every bit of you that may touch the house, from the hair of your head to the soles of your feet. Then enter here and do the same for every man of us.'

As the blood was rubbed on each Fenian man, he came unstuck from seat and floor and wall. In this way all were released except Conan. They came to him last, spread out on the hearthstone, and by that time only a smear and stain were left in the cups. It was enough to free the most of him, but none was left for the back of his head. The hair and the skin of his head till stuck to the hearth.

When they were loose, Finn and his men set off rejoicing, and they had not gone very far when they heard the loud voice of Conan behind. As he came up they saw that the back of his head was stripped, without any tuft of hair and with a long bare patch of skin. In his effort to free himself, after the rest left him, he gave his head a great fierce pull and abandoned to the hearthstone his hair and his skin. From that day forth all men called him Conan Mael, or Bald Conan without Hair.

With glad hearts Finn and his men reached home. And then Finn gave word and oath that he would never again engage a wandering lad.

FINN AND THE
WISDOM OF THE WORLD

On a fine day, Finn and his men were hunting in the mountains of Donegal. All day they had chased a deer high and low. But they lost her and they were tired.

'Let us face for home, men,' said Finn, 'or the night will catch us before we reach our beds.'

They were not far down the hillside when a black fog fell on them. So they sat where they were, not knowing east from west.

'A fog like this is a horror to us,' said Finn. 'I'm afraid, lad, that we are astray for the night.'

But keen-eyed Diarmuid was peering about, and through a chink in the fog he saw the weak gleam of a lime-white house. Gladly, the Fenians hurried to it, but found there only a little withered old man, and a sheep tied along by the wall.

234

The old man looked up from the edge of the hearth and gave Finn a weary welcome.

'Upon my soul,' said Diarmuid in a low voice, 'it is unlikely that we will get any ease in this hovel.'

The old man called to a woman below to bring food, and then there came in a fine handsome girl, as lovely as the day. And it did not take her long to spread a big table with all manner of food and drink. Finn sat at the head of the table and every man found meat before him. But hardly a bite was in their mouths when the sheep that was tethered along the wall broke the hemp rope, upended the table, and pitched every scrap of food onto the floor.

'Devil take you,' roared Conan. 'You've made a fine mess of the dinner, and we badly in need of it.'

'Rise up, Conan,' said Finn, 'and tie the sheep.'

Conan caught the sheep by the top of her head and tried to drag her to the wall. But he could not move her, though his heart might burst in the attempt.

'By heavens,' he said, 'here's this great warrior that I am, and I can't tie up a sheep. Let someone else move her.'

First Diarmuid tried, and then every one of them. But it was no use.

'Shame on you all,' said the old man. 'Great and brave as you are, there's not a one of you can tie a poor sheep with a bit of rope.'

Then he rose from the edge of the hearth and hobbled down the floor. Six pints of ashes fell from the backside of his trousers, from his long lying on the hearth. He took the sheep by the scruff, and tugged her easily to the wall, and tied the rope. When the men of the Fianna saw this, they felt fear and trembling, for he could do himself what brave warriors had failed to do. Quietly the old man returned to his place by the fire and called for the young woman to bring more food.

It was not long before there was more meat and drink on the table.

'Start eating, lads,' said the old man, 'you'll have no more trouble.'

When they were full, and resting their bellies in the glow of the fire, Finn saw the young woman sitting apart. He had a desire to talk to her and went down the room to her.

'Finn Mac Cool,' said she sternly, 'you had me once and you won't have me again.'

Finn turned back with a red face, and then Diarmuid went down to her. But he got the same answer, and so did every one of the Fenians. When Oisin was the last to try, she took him by the hand and led him in front of the company.

'Finn Mac Cool,' she said, 'you and the Fenians were ever famous for strength and courage, yet still each one of you failed to tie the sheep. 'Tis an unusual sheep. She is Strength. And the old man beyond the hearth is Death. As strong as the sheep is, the old man will overcome her. In the same way, Death will come upon you, strong as you all are. And I am Youth. Each of you had me once, but you never will again. Now I will give you any wish.'

Finn was the first to ask. He wished to lose the smell of clay, which had clung to him ever since he sinned with a woman now dead. Then Diarmuid wanted a love-spot on his body, to bewitch young women. Oscar asked for an unbreakable thong for his sling. And Conan wished to be invulnerable, and for the power to kill hundreds in battle.

'Alas,' cried Diarmuid when he heard this, 'that Conan should ever have the use of such a power! He is such a vicious, ill-tempered man, he may not leave a Fenian alive.'

So Conan was granted the power but he could not use it, except once at the Battle of Ventry, when he looked at his enemies through his fingers and killed every one of them.

When all the wishes had been granted, Finn turned to see what his men thought of their gifts. And when he looked again, he found himself and the Fenians standing on the mountainside, with nothing but sheep and goats grazing nearby.

FINN TOWARDS THE
END OF HIS AGE

Now, after Finn had been some long time in the
house of Conan of Ceann Slieve, he thought he had
been questioned more than enough. At last, he was
impatient and turned-aside.

'Prepare a bed for myself and Finndealbh,' said he, 'for you
have asked enough, O Conan, concerning the plight and
troubles of Finn and the Fenians. The back end of the night
is upon us, and it is time for more blissful things.'

Finally, Finn slept. But a bad vision infected his dream, and
he sprang thrice from his bed in fear.

'I saw the Tuatha De Danann,' he said to Finndealbh. 'They
were raising a quarrel against me and making a bloody
carnage of my Fenians.'

As for the Fenians themselves, they had no tidings of Finn
so they pitched camp where they were. Early next day, Bran

Beg and Bran Mor went to Mac an Reith to learn where Finn lay. Then the two Brans went quickly to the house of Conan of Ceann Slieve. And when they came in to Finn, they reproached him for going forward with his wedding-feast without the presence of the Fenians.

'We have a banquet prepared and ready at Allen in Leinster,' said Bran Mor. 'Let us go and partake of it.'

So they all went to the hall in Allen, and the Fenian men were intent on pleasure that night. But they had not been long there when they saw Cairbre, son of Cormac, son of Conn the Hundred Fighter, shape his way directly to where they were.

'No good thing is coming to us,' said Finn, 'since our *geasa* forbids us to break up our entertainment. Yet this son of the king of Ireland will expect us to make way for him at the head of the feast.'

'We will not do so,' said Oisin. 'But rather let us give up half the hall for him and keep half for us.'

This was willingly done, but certain of the Tuatha De Danann took it as an insult.

'Is this how Finn Mac Cool makes disrespect to us,' said one of them, 'while he himself possesses the woman who had been promised to Fatha Mac Avric, the third best man of all the Tuatha De Danann?'

These men departed in the dawn and went to Finbarr at Magh Feabhail, and they told him of the insults and wrongs offered by Finn to the people of the Tuatha De Danann.

Then Finbarr collected six powerful battalions, from all parts of Ireland, and they gathered at Loch Derg. This muster took place on the very day that Conan of Ceann Slieve himself gave a wedding-feast for his daughter and Finn.

Finn was coming to the feast with none but a few of the men of the family of Morna.

'Never, O Goll,' said Finn, 'have I had such fear and misgivings to attend a wedding-feast. My forces are few in number. I have a fore knowledge that evil broods over me. The Tuatha De Danann are ready to slaughter my people.'

Then Goll Mac Morna promised faithfully to defend him,

and they went forward to the wedding-feast in the house of Conan. In the hall, Finn sat by the door with Goll on his right and Finndealbh to his left.

At this time Finbarr and the warriors of the Tuatha De Danann were covering themselves with a magic mist and marching without delay, invisibly, steadily, powerfully, to a place on the plain next to the house of Conan. But they were not confident to fight that day.

'What use for us to be here,' they asked, 'since Goll Mac Morna himself defends Finn against us?'

'Goll shall not protect him,' replied Ethne the druidess, 'for I will beguile Finn from the house, whatever care is put over him.'

She went to the house and saw Finn just within the door.

'Who is that before my face?' she said.

'It is I myself,' replied Finn.

'I put you under a *geasa*, which you shall not break as you are a true hero,' said she, 'to come forth to me immediately.'

Finn would not break the bonds of a *geasa* and went outside, though none in the house but Caoilte saw him leave. Then the warriors of the Tuatha De Danann let fly a flock of dark birds with fiery beaks into the fort of Conan. These birds perched on the chests of those within and so scorched and tortured them that men, women and children fled in all directions. Canana, wife of Conan, ran with flaming clothes into the river and was drowned.

Then Ethne said to Finn, 'Run a race with me for your freedom.'

'What distance will that be?' asked Finn.

'From the forest of Two-Wild-Boars in the west, to the Great Ford in the east.'

Thus it was agreed. They ran and ran but Finn was leading toward the ford, and Caoilte, who had followed him out from the house, was chasing hard. Finn was urging him forward.

'Shame on your running, O Caoilte,' he called out, 'for your small amount of swiftness. A woman is leaving you behind.'

Then Caoilte sprang forward and made a most exemplary leap onto the druidess, and struck his shoulder against her chest. As she staggered, he turned about and made a slash of his sword to her waist, so that he cut her into two parts.

'Win victory and blessings, O Caoilte,' cried Finn. 'Many is the good blow you have struck in your time, but never a better one than that.'

They faced about and as quick as they could ran back to the green of Ceann Slieve. They found that the Tuatha De Danann had thrown off the cover of the magic mist and were drawn up in warlike ranks.

'We are fallen in the thick of enemies,' said Finn to Caoilte. Then back to back they stood against waves of attack till groans of hurt and faintness broke from them.

This noise of unequal combat came to Goll and wrung his heart. He called to his friends, and rallied the household of Conan and his sons, and they all rushed upon the green in a dense body, intent upon great feats of arms and carnage and murder.

Now Goll Mac Morna, the chief of champions, the body-mangler, the terrible thunderer, was enraged. Like a towering mountain under his grey shield was he in battle. He laid low the leaders, and crushed the bodies of their nobles, and burst through all enemy ranks. He shortened limbs and emptied skulls till he reached the pillar of the opposition, Finbarr himself. They fought like great lions, but Finbarr could not withstand the heavy, double-handed strokes of Goll, and he fell.

Chief slew chief, and good men went down before the blows from good men. Few were the battles in Ireland fought with such dreadful spite and force. None wished, or was so without honour, to yield or retreat a single step. For these were the two most hard-fighting bodies of men to be found in any of the four corners of the globe: that is to say, the manly, bloody, robust, unbowed Fenians of Finn Mac Cool, and the white-toothed, large-limbed, grim-armed warriors of the Tuatha De Danann. They were both well-nigh finished before the sun set on that battle.

At last, in the declining of the day, all the Fenians of Ireland who had missed the battle were seen approaching. When they saw this, the Tuatha De Danann wrapped themselves in the magic mist and melted away most suddenly. Finn himself was in fainting fits from the pain of his wounds. And Oisin despaired at the great number of the fallen. Of Finn's thousand heroes, all but one hundred were slain. And even these were maimed, weak and wounded.

As to Finn Mac Cool, he was carried to the house at Ceann Slieve where he remained under cure for a month and a fortnight. Then he and his few followers limped home to Allen in Leinster. And they stayed a long time quietly in Allen, with the memory of their hurts and their wounds still painfully upon them.

OISIN
AFTER THE FIANNA

Oisin, son of Finn, survived after the time of the Fenians. He lived in the house of his daughter. He was blind, deaf and limping, and there were nine oak skewers in his belly. He ate the tribute that holy Patrick had over Ireland. He was telling the old histories, and they were writing them.

They killed a grand stag, and stripped the shank, and brought him the bone.

'Did you ever see a shank thicker than that in the Fenians?' they asked.

'I saw a bone of the blackbird's chick in which that would be lost,' he replied after he had felt the bone.

But they said, 'There's nothing but lies in what you tell us.'

Then he caught hold of the books in a rage, and he set them in the fire. But his daughter rescued the books, and quenched them, and kept them.

Oisin was wailing and asking for company. 'Would that even the worst lad and dog in the Fianna,' he cried, 'might lay a hand on my chest.'

He felt a weight and said, 'What's this?'

''Tis the son of the Red One,' came the answer. There was another weight at his feet, and that was the son of the Little Yellow One.

In the morning they arose and Oisin asked one of the lads to take him to the glen. When they reached it, Oisin took a wooden whistle from his pocket and played on it.

'What goes past on yonder mountain?' asked blind Oisin.

'I see deer on it,' said the lad.

'What sort of deer?'

'I see some slender and grey.'

'Let them pass. Those are the seed of the swift elk. But what see you now?'

'I see some gaunt and grizzled.'

'Let them pass. Those are the seed of the fierce red deer. But what see you now?'

'I see some heavy and sleek.'

'Then unleash the dog.' And away went the dog after the deer.

'Little Yellow One,' said Oisin, 'when the hound has caught a dozen we shall check him.' And when that time came, Oisin played on his whistle and checked the hound.

'If the pup is sated with chase,' said he, 'he will come quietly. If not, he will come with his gape open.'

But the hound was coming with his gape open and his tongue out at his mouth, so Oisin said, 'Catch hold of my hand and try to put it in his gape, or he will have us.'

The lad put Oisin's hand in the mouth of the hound, and he shook the throat out of the dog. Then the lad dragged the dead deer to a rushy knoll, and when he had taken them all there were nine stags on it. That was enough for Oisin alone, so the lad's portion was lost. Oisin delved into the rushy knoll, and in it was the great cauldron of the Fenians. The lad put a fire under the cauldron and in a little time the stags were cooked.

'Touch not the meat,' said Oisin, 'till first I take my fill.'

Oisin began upon the animals, and as he ate each one he took one of the skewers out of his belly. Six were eaten, but Oisin found no more. The lad had taken three.

'Have you done this to me?' Oisin asked.

'I did it,' said the lad, 'for you took so many and I had need of a few.'

'Well, then,' said Oisin, 'now let us face for home.'

The lad caught him under the arm and away they went. As Oisin felt they were nearing the house, he said, 'Is the house close by?'

'It is,' said the lad.

'Would the shout of a man reach the house from where we are?'

'It would reach it.'

'Set my foot straight toward the door.' And the lad did this.

When he was sure that he was set toward the house, Oisin suddenly caught hold of the lad, put his hands to his throat, and killed him.

'Now,' said he, 'neither you nor another will ever tell tales of the son of Finn again.'

THE LAMENTATION
OF OISIN FOR
FINN MAC COOL

The battles of Gavra and Ollarba had been fought, and the Fianna were for the most part destroyed. Those who remained scattered in small bands throughout Ireland, till only two good warriors were left: Oisin, son of Finn, and Caoilte Mac Ronan.

Oisin lived on, even into the days of the blessed Patrick, the apostle to the Gaels. That religious man said benediction over the fort of Finn Mac Cool, and he sprinkled the holy water that drove away a thousand legions of demons into the *shee*-hills and the skalps at the outer borders of the land.

Demons departed forthwith, in all directions. And all about Oisin was the quiet and holy order of the church. But his heart was not in it, and he yearned for the hunt and the hounds, the feasting and wooing, the passage of arms, and the bravery and the blood of battle.

Then Oisin gave a long despairing cry:

It is grief to me, O Patrick,
Though God is gracious and loving,
To speak no more of Finn –
Most melancholy to me – and of the Fenians.

Farewell to wooing and to hunting,
Farewell to drinking and sweet music,
Farewell to fights and to battle,
Farewell, moreover, to sharp blades.

Farewell to speed and strength,
Farewell to slaughter and clean wounds,
Farewell to far lands and to returning,
Farewell to gifts and to single combat.

Farewell to feasts and the full cup,
Farewell to running and to leaping,
Farewell to the chase on every rough hill,
Farewell to the fights of mighty men.

Alas! is not my grief a piteous tale,
That I am fasting in the church of the poor?
Scarce of bread and scant of food,
My body lacks all strength and power.

Farewell, O Finn, again and again,
A hundred times, O Fenian king!
For you indeed would conquer my thirst,
Unlike thin porridge the holy clerics eat.

INDEX